TWO-WAY TRAFFIC

By Joel Lieber

Two-Way → ← Traffic

joel lieber

doubleday & company, inc.
garden city, new york
1972

TWO-WAY TRAFFIC

I
from notebook one

"Don't go to Switzerland," said the voice on the phone. "You'll do yourself more good if you stay in New York and face up to things."

"How about Montreal? I have a good friend up there."

Decide between Bud, painter, my age, bachelor, a good, good friend, and my brother Ben, financier, investment counselor, mutual-funder and his wife Arlette, thirty-five, business partner, French: another decision I can't make.

"Well?"

"Canada *is* closer," I admit.

"Besides, this is no time for your relatives. . . . Can I ask you something? Do you know what time it is?"

"I know, I know."

Seven fifteen in the morning. The voice confirms it.

"But I already bought the ticket for Lausanne yesterday."

"Was that smart?"

"It was impulsive. It was a decision." A decision. Silence at the other end. "It was a decision."

"I tell you what," came the voice on the phone, "five days in Montreal would be better for you than two weeks in Switzerland."

"Right. Okay. I'll cash in the ticket this morning, go to Montreal, and see you next week."

"Good. Now try to think clearly. Simply. Unambiguously."

Seven o'clock. Twelve hours later. Aboard Swissair 133 for Geneva. Switzerland is farther *away* than Montreal. I am exhausted. I have been for three months now. I can hear myself not thinking straight. My apartment stinks with bad memories, stinks of a bed where two children were created and where sleep is no longer possible, stinks of a wife who has turned love into hate, stinks of a desk at which I can no longer work, stinks of sweat everywhere, stinks of black flecks of New York crap around the windows, of confused closets, dirty laundry, papers everywhere, unopened mail, unpaid bills, dying plants in a deserted living room, dying fish in the fish tank, an empty children's room, an empty pantry. Letters

from lawyers asking for their retainers. Even my
dogs aren't there. Nine years of marriage: done and
gone, eight years okay and the ninth insane, self-
indulgent and stoned.

Question: Who is more insane? My manic spaced-
out wife, becoming fourteen again, becoming a
stranger to me? Or me? The way I've degenerated
to depression, become sluggish, disturbing to everyone around me and doing nothing, ceasing to function, losing my will. In the second year of my third
decade somebody else has come to live inside me and
I hate that visitor.

Thirty-five planes on the runway in front of us.
Dinner is served at 12:30 A.M. We are still sitting
here, for five hours. I decline dinner. The red-
cheeked one is indifferent. I sit next to a lady from
the midwest on a tour. She eats the meal and finishes
the dessert at one o'clock in the morning. She doesn't
leave over a thing.

Geneva: my brother, in a three-piece banker's
pinstripe. My sister-in-law, trim and smart and Eu-
ropean and long-skirted. "See? No customs. That's
the Swiss for you," he says. "You should have
brought some gold or watches." I am silent. They've
got a doctor for me in Neufchâtel. A Swiss Jewish
shrink. I am impressed by the cleanliness of my
brother's car. He does 160 km on the Geneva to
Lausanne road. It can do more, he reassures me with
a grin, but if you get into an accident, the insurance

company don't pay if you were over the speed limit.
When the folks were over here they didn't know
from kilometers. Dad suspected I was going very
fast and one day he looked it up in his guide book
and confronted me with it. Put on your seat belt.

I refuse. Let it happen. I don't care. I am wondering if this Swiss trip is a good idea.

I have my own room at their apartment that over-
looks Lake Geneva. Lac Leman s'il vous plait. We
eat upon arrival. What meal should I be eating?

You look skinny, they tell me. Your beard is
sparse.

Paula's become a macrobiotic.

Ah oui?

You didn't bring a camera.

I shrug.

They are too polite to exchange glances. They are
beginning to see what has happened: I have let go.

Is there anything worse than this? Maybe two divorces. Or three. I mean for me and the way I am
with my work, and with the kids and not being able
to cook and hating laundromats and supermarkets.
She used to take care of all that. I haven't even
moved out yet. I only helped them move away for
the summer to the beach.

Back in New York a little Catholic girl from the
eighth floor waters the plants in the apartment while
I am away. She feeds the fish too. She is timid and

reliable and probably conscientious at catechism. Who will she marry?

Lausanne: so orderly, so stable, in comparison to my mad state. So clean and neat. Beautifully dressed shop windows.

They like antiques, brother and sister-in-law. Saturday, after twelve hours in bed (and four hours' sleep—I awake exhausted) we hit the road. It's so clean here! There's no refuse. They are looking for a conference table but it must be an antique. We make several stops out in the country. This table is too expensive, that one is too low, too short, too dirty, too small. Sandy, their dog, has to pee everywhere.

"Merci madame. . . . Bonjour . . . combien d' . . . oh *non*."

We visit the castle at Gruyères. Crowded as hell. We all listen to the musicians and watch the flag-throwers. They even have some conference tables at an antique shop there. We have views from the terrace and views from behind the cannons and views from rooms filled with medieval torture instruments. She buys cheese and butter and we have hot chocolate at a restaurant inside the château. The cream is as thick as sour cream.

Next day I am dragged off to see the psychiatrist who has helped both of them. The road to Neufchâtel is forty miles of farms and villages, hillside meadows, Opels, Fiats, BMWs, Volkswagens, Peugeots, cows.

"I am a Fribourgeoise and in Fribourg all the
cows are black and white. Look at these brown cows
they have here," says my belle-soeur.

How green it is! Swiss summer.

I've slept, really slept, maybe two or three hours
a night for the last four months, in case that explains
any of this.

Yverdon: with a race track and an antiques museum and a castle. I didn't bring a camera. I don't
even have any pictures to show Tommy. Why? I
must have been thinking of something else. I forgot
to think. I don't know how any more.

The way they pile their firewood. It's so neat. The
farms. The flags with red fields and white crosses.
Orange-topped roofs wearing TV antennas. Motor-
bikes. You only have to be fourteen to have a license
here. The cars all have CH on their backs, Confed-
eration Helvetia. Ben drives like an Italian, laughs
my sister-in-law. He is getting to be a better Swiss
than the Swiss. Now he is getting Italian too from
all those trips. (He has lived here five years.)

The doctor is really Jewish! A Jewish Swiss shrink.
Imagine. He looks like a diplomat. He's suave. He's
friendly. He wants to help.

"So tell me your story," he says.

–M B –1764 –tb, mysteriously carved on the
back of his antique desk, facing me. Very distracting.

I keep coming back to them as I tell him my story. He listens, writes down some stuff, seems astonished here and there.

"She is clearly an intoxicomaniac. . . . You left *her* with the children? . . . Depressed people like yourself are more depressed in the morning. I'll give you something for that. And to sleep. . . . Nine-tenths of the American psychiatrists and psychologists are criminals. . . . Imagine, not to have placed her in a clinic. She should have been withdrawn from drugs. . . . Of course you are not thinking clearly. You have the look of a person not well. Your pride, your ego has suffered. Attack back! . . . If you do not have the strength postpone the divorce decisions. In any case have a good lawyer. . . . American law is different from Swiss law. We don't give the woman so much here, especially when she breaks the marriage. . . . I regret I cannot see her professionally. . . . Clearly, she is regressing to an infantile stage. . . . But most women would be happy with a husband's success such as yours, is that not so? Instead, she attacks you. She must feel unnecessary now. . . . It is a tragedy, yes? A real tragedy when you suddenly lose your environment. In such cases fatigue and depression are not uncommon. . . . And please be careful about the guilt. It is one thing to *feel* guilty. It is another thing to *become* guilty. You understand? . . . I am at your

disposal. . . . Don't forget the prescription. You
need it to get your life moving again."

Outside he and Arlette greet each other happily.
First they laugh and smile and he inquires after my
brother's business. Then they lower voices and start
speaking faster, discussing my case. She nods: Yes,
yes of course. Food and sleep and exercise. No, he is
not working. His wife? Yes, I knew her. I'll take him
climbing and swimming and boating.

In the pastry shop in Neufchâtel the baker's wife
hears us speaking English. "But I am from Fribourg," says Arlette when the woman exclaims, "Oh
but you speak beautiful French as well." A wise guy
overhears and says, "Do you know why the birds fly
upside down over Fribourg? So they won't see the
misery of the town."

Mafiosa, Arlette mutters, laughing, gathering her
packages.

One stop for the butcher for sausage, a check on
two antiques stores for conference tables, and then
back in the car.

She's a fast driver. She was Miss Switzerland in
1951, a lion-tamer's assistant, TV actress, an au
père, tobogganist, dancer, model, cosmetician, de-
partment-store buyer, and God-knows-what-else.

"I first met the doctor in 1957. I was going with a
guy for seven years. He had three children from the

divorce. His wife was—how do you call it—a nymphomaniac? And I was completely lost. The doctor told me not to marry this one. Nor any Swiss man, for that matter. So there you are; I married with your brother (*wiz your bruzere*)."

She wears a leather glove on her left hand when she drives, the right is free for her Salems, which she nearly chain-smokes. Chin-out, somewhat military behind the wheel, changes gears beautifully and never fails to signal. She's a better, that is, smoother driver than Ben. Possibly the best lady driver I know. She points out places where she has nearly had accidents and where the local tomato farmers intercepted tomatoes coming from Italy. She tries. She really tries with me. He got a nice girl, my brother. House spotless, beds starchy, bathrooms like a hotel. She is a hausfrau, businesswoman, racing-car driver, gourmet cook, fantastic in a bikini. He is lucky to have her. She is so cool and capable. I never knew her until this trip. I always thought mine was superior to his. Mine who I always thought superior is now inferior, uncivilized, dizzy, doggy, crazy, bitchy. Maybe that's part of the trouble, thinking of her as *mine*.

Why me? Am I such a bad guy? I was minding my own business, working, tending this and that, when she flipped out, slept in her clothes for weeks, stared into candles, painted on balloons, and decided she hated me, embarked on a new personality.

("We must formulate a plan of action," said the shrink, "but if you are not capable of it right now—")

It's like Abe Fortas said: like stepping off a curb and being hit by a car. It was that sudden. I'm a statistic. A visitor to my children.

We stop at a castle, Chillon, a big one. "In the dungeon," explains the guide, "they threw the executed ones right out the window into the lake."

"I was here twenty years ago," says Arlette. "Every Swiss child visits Chillon."

Byron stopped by on a night in June, 1815. The plaque in the prison commemorates his visit. His boat was caught in a storm and he was moved to write a poem. In the gift shop they sell copies: Lord Byron: *The Prisoner of Chillon.*

Eternal Spirit of the Chainless mind!
Brightest in dungeons, Liberty! thou art,
For there thy habitation is the heart—
The heart which love of thee alone can bind.

Twenty bullshit pages all about bursting chains and dungeon dew. Not one of Byron's better. Arlette buys me a copy. I get a cowbell for my son and for my daughter a little box that makes a cow sound when you turn it over. We ride in silence. The rest of the way back to Lausanne my head is going so fast and confused I can't speak. Is he learning to

swim this summer? What does he ask about me?
What does she say to him? Is the baby getting bow-
legged and toeing-in like her brother? I find I'm not
concerned about what she's doing and who she's seeing. I have, by turns, loved her, pitied her, hated
her, envied her, abused her, laughed at her, ignored
her, taken her for granted, cried at her. No wonder.
I keep looking for it to add up. Six months ago the
handwriting was on the wall, but the shrink said no,
just symptoms, manifestations of her illness, she
doesn't know what's she doing or what she wants,
don't take it at face value, don't take what she says
literally. What she does literally. Don't take it per-
sonally. Let her use drugs. Let her be one day a
photographer, the next day a painter, the next a
sculptress, the next a dancer, the next a Yoga, the
next a macrobiotic cook. Indulge her, indulge her.
I should have kicked her ass out. I didn't. I followed
professional advice.

Being Jewish is no excuse for what you're taking,
advised a friend.

When she got going she even outdid me in selfishness, at which I had built a sizable reputation.

I shave sloppily. My pants are loose. My hair has
dandruff. Pimples, bleeding gums, pains in the back
of the head. Sleep is for other people.

Their balcony faces the lake. Lac Leman. Sail-
boats posing. Water-skiers. Very little noise.

A church bell every fifteen minutes. Across the lake
the French mountains, Évian. A cluster of pinhead
lights at night. The big red light is the big casino,
my brother tells me. When out of the living room I
hear him discussing my trip to the doctor with
Arlette, gravely.

("Your will is ill," said the Man. "You've lost
your desire. But it is only temporary. I've seen such
cases. I predict a recovery.")

When a storm comes, she tells me, they flash a
light and ring a bell, warning the boats, but the
boats often overturn. I see it often. I nod.

Am I eating here! After two months of mostly
grain, rice and sesame seeds with soy sauce. Entre-
côtes, coffee, juices, ice cream, legs of lamb, fish and
chips, creamy sauces, strawberries and cream, choc-
olates, dried fruit. My brother's got himself a Jewish
mother, this Fribourgeoisie, who is also Catholic,
with a lady's manners, and strong, tidy ways.

She won't stop feeding me. Nuts, herring, crackers.
I'd like to send my children CARE packages, half
of what she makes. (I have been advised to take her
to court over the diet; depends how skinny the kids
are when I get back.) I haven't been this stuffed
since thirteen days on the S.S. *Olympic*. For breakfast I eat as much as I ate on some recent entire
days. This morning, orange juice, Familia (she
added some of her own sliced peaches, raisins and
apples), rolls with butter and jam, and eggs, a soup-

bowl of coffee. Three hours later came potato soup, braised beef and sauce, spinach, salad, raspberries and cream. In between meals she fills me with M&Ms, fruits, pieces of chocolate. Dinner today— I can't go on. My stomach sags under the weight. My blood is changing; more like clogging. Exercise, I tell her. I need exercise. My brother nods his approval. Take him to the farm. Climb. Take my hiking shoes, here. I nod. Okay. Whatever you say. I consent to any offer of help.

Anguish, suffering, sleeplessness, worry, anxiety, tension: my companions. Why does it persist? Why can't I make them go away? I don't know what to do or where. I can live anywhere, theoretically. Near my children or far. Lausanne. Jerusalem. California. Nepal. To name just four.

Has the unknown always scared me like this? Was I able to cover it up when I controlled the situation?

Excitement tonight: a lightning storm. We watch the explosions over the lake where we had been boating this afternoon, earlier. There was a lot of garbage in the water. Swimming didn't taste too good at all. But it was cold and good exercise. We were a mile out when we had to start rowing to get in—the lightning popping down south across the lake in France. From the balcony I could have played Ben Franklin with his key. My son would have enjoyed the view; a view of five open miles of whitecaps and skies; sizzling electric bolts. At least I

could have brought my movie camera to show him
pictures.

Why aren't I with him instead of his loony
mother? He gets pissed when there's no orange juice
for breakfast (too yin, she says, or is it yang; I forget
which). My brother asks, "What kind of influence
will he have with a woman who sits around night
after night smoking pot and painting on balloons?
She'll drive him nuts. Send him over here." "How?"
I ask. Tell the lawyer to show proof that—prepare
a case for it—make a written list of the problems
and attack them one at a—incorporate yourself in
Lichtenstein—stay here another week—

Fights and lawsuits and custody battles, settlement
payments and moving vans. My brother bandies the
real words around; for me they are not real. I am
not ready. Somewhere I have lost my strength. Why
don't I act? Why don't I react? Why didn't I react
earlier on, instinctively? There must be a reason. I
just don't know it yet. Either I hoped I'd awake one
morning and everything would be fine—or, I listened
to the shrink's advice, that this whole mess was to
be treated as her sickness, her identity crisis, her
adolescent rebellion—or I am sick for not reacting to
assaults on my person(ality).

This Lausanne place: ashtrays are always empty,
the streets are never dirty, faces clear and calm and
sober, cars spic-and-span, shopkeepers polite and dig-

nified. Make a mistake and overpay and they chase you down the streets with your change.

Today we tackled another castle—the Conan Doyle Castle at Lucens. It has a replica of the messy consultant room where Sherlock Holmes worked on Baker Street, a Victorian room with photos of General Gordon, raincoats, old newspapers, laboratory equipment, Doctor Watson's hat and cape. "After the Bible, more people have read Sherlock Holmes books than any other work." Is that true? How do you check that? How about Shakespeare? Sir Arthur's son, Adrian Conan Doyle, lives here. He runs the château like a big store. Adrian is tall, distinguished-looking, wears a sheepskin coat and drives a snazzy sports car. He delivers a talk in the torture room. ("On your left here we have the original iron maiden of Nuremburg. Notice the spikes of varying length as the door swings shut. . . .") His wife sells English editions of his father's works—along with small, medium and large Sherlock Holmes hats. *The Hound of the Baskervilles* is still the biggest seller, she reports. Outside the boutique her nine-month-old Pekingese pulls on his leash. Adrian's voice drifts down from the top of the staircase: "These killer sharks were caught by Sir Arthur when he was . . ." His wife tells me they've put central heating in the wing of the castle where they live, but they only stay there till November. Then they go to Mallorca. How come all this

Sherlock Holmes stuff is in Switzerland? I ask. She
tells me how her father-in-law loved Switzerland. I
buy two books and three post cards in her shop.

"We ought to take him to the restaurant at St.
Saphorin," says my brother. "See that village up
there? One of the best restaurants in the area."

"What am I doing here?" I hear my voice ask
aloud.

"You need a rest. You're not thinking clearly.
You're not functioning."

Here I'm functioning?

"You're in better shape than when you arrived.
You're sleeping—"

"Pills—"

"Still, they get you to sleep, right? . . . Chou, you
give such good neck jobs. That's how it all started
with us, remember, Chou? Up at Great Barrington,
that first weekend, skiing?" (And I remember how
mine got started, on a date at the West End bar, in
1960, and no neck jobs.)

The traffic is heavy. A Taunus with Geneva plates
has been in front of us for ten minutes. "My friend
was about to throw a pack of cigarettes on the
ground—from his car. Uh-oh, better not," he said,
"I'm in Switzerland. . . . A friend of mine from
Italy, last week—you can picnic in a peasant's field
here, but damned if the guy who owns the place

doesn't poke his nose around the next morning to see
if you've made a mess. . . . If you turn left you lose
priority here. . . . Montreux is Miami and Nice together." (A sign: Buy or option Eurotel and it gives
you 20 per cent discount at other Eurotels in Europe.) "Down there if you like we can take the boat
later. . . . Here's Villeneuve. We're at the end of
the lake." (I recall Villeneuve on a sign in a railway station when we took the train from Lausanne
to Nice, on our honeymoon. I recall the way we slept
on the benches in the train compartment that
night.)

"What am I doing here? What does this have to
do with anything? What am I *doing* here?"

"You're resting for the fight when you go back.
You've got some big decisions to make and right now
you're incapable of making them."

Okay, keep driving. The BP stations, fourteen
Hôtels des Raisens, Total stations, Migral stations,
castles, vineyards, head-down motorcyclists, VWs,
Consuls.

"These drivers from Belgium and the Netherlands
can really drive you up the wall." (C. Kaufman,
Chalets and Antiquities.) "They've got a great syn-
agogue in Lausanne." On the back of a Renault:
Faites amour, pas guerre. Shell-shocked is how I feel.
"Voilà, les Alpes." Ah, the Chamonix Railroad, see
it on the mountain over there? . . . Over there the
Grand St. Bernard pass. . . . This is Valle. . . . See

the glaciers up ahead? . . . That's past Sion. They
go skiing there in the summer in bathing suits. . . .
They say it took a million years for the water to
make that gorge there. They call the waterfall *Pig-
Vache.*"

Who has the priority over here? Going up or going
down?

Up, she says. Always up.

Vex: pine and spruce forests, chalets and ski stations. Two thousand meters now. Voilà. Thyon. We
park the car. Let's climb. But first some sandwiches.
Picnic. O.K. Out of the trunk materializes wine,
cheese, sausage, blankets, chairs. The efficient one
forgets nothing. Then we climb the mountain. My
brother has on corduroy knickers and red socks. Arlette and I are in tennis sneakers. Sloping meadows
of violet and daffodil. Their dog is happy here, Sandy,
black and white collie, two cases of distemper under
his belt.

We follow the zigzag path under the ski lift; she
had wanted to take the lift and walk along the top
ridge but the lift isn't running today. We are heading toward the snow path. It's about fifteen hundred
meters, they think. She usually contradicts his esti-
mates of distances. Then he concedes she is probably
right. Odd. My ankles are sagging but she goes on
like a mountain goat. I click off a few pictures on
Ben's Rollei, so I have something to show Tom.
What's the first thing you get? Ben asks me, climb-

ing. An interim separation? I don't answer. I look at the sky, all blue. Down in the valley a plane: odd to have your feet on the ground and look down at a plane. Above us a glider is circling. My wife's father flies a plane. Everything reminds me. Everything. Walking and walking and walking, up and up and up. Out of breath. Stopping every fifteen minutes. Finally, after four hours, we get to the snow, a patch of thirty or forty meters amid the green. We take pictures of each other holding snowballs aloft. From another path comes a family, the boy about three, on his father's back, and the girl, maybe six, carrying a knapsack. I feel a choke in my throat. The sight of them takes away what little pleasure there was in reaching the snow. Arlette notices the looks on my face and throws me a snowball. I let it hit me and then walk away from the sounds of the children playing in the snow.

Fifteen meters farther up I sit on a rock and look at the villages on the facing slope of the next mountain. I can't resist looking at those children again. My sense of loss is overwhelming. For the first time in a long time I feel the hot, sticky grab in my throat. Tears form in there but they don't reach the surface.

Next day, the doctor again.
"You look better."

"I feel worse."

"Don't expect magic. The anti-depression pills
are working? You are sleeping? You are working?"
No.

She should have been in a clinic, he says. Can
you do calisthenics in the morning? Do you have a
religion? Friends you can stay with?

I know all this. It's a waste of time.

From there Arlette takes me to a friend's farm to
spend the night. She loves to drive. Ben has to go to
Brussels on business. The friend is a banker, my
brother's business partner. She stops at a St. Imry
shop—steaks, chops, melon, coffee, wine. The farm
is very isolated. We keep opening and closing gates
as we drive through—for the cows. At the house, a
new two-story chalet on the side of a hill, equipped
with gas range and stereo and freezer and central
heating. We plug in fuses and open windows.

The furniture is mostly antiques. Outside an immense quiet. Only the tinkle of cowbells. We take a
hike through the pastures, the dog, Sandy, chasing
cows, barking and nipping. Cow shit everywhere.

At dinner she tells me stories of a party here last
year with a hundred thirty people. I tell her I'm
ready to go back in a couple of days. "But you've
only been here a week. I hate to see you go back like
this." We build a fire and talk for seven hours: my
working at home, my wife's contributions, the children, the fights, her behavior during the winter,

what the drugs had to do with it, the regrets, my
inaction, my fatigue. Rehashing it all. Arlette asks
good questions. Do I dream? she asks. Last night I
had one: a fight with Paula in which I threw out all
the macrobiotic food and threw her out. In another
dream that night I fought with my father, with
whom, lately, I had become somewhat friendly
again.

"Tell me about your sex life," she asks. I tell her
mine and she doesn't really tell me hers. "You have
been in love before her?" Once or twice, but maybe
not even really with her. "Three days after meeting
her you ask her to marry. Three months after that
you are married. Right? Not good." (The doctor remarked on the same thing, making a sour face.)

"Sometimes I think I shouldn't be married. Your
brother is very selfish. He hurts me a lot sometimes."
We are intimate and confidant-ish. She keeps replac-
ing logs in the fireplace. I smoke her Salems and
drink the unseen host's wine. Cowbells tinkle outside. "You are certain it is done?" *Certain*.

"I am unhappy when I am not caring for someone
and someone is not caring for me." She is sleepy.
I am sleepy. We talk on. I hope my brother is good to
her. I like her. We cover small families versus large.
She is the youngest of eight children. Her brothers
and sisters all stayed peasants. She got out. I tell
her about the hospital. She is curious. But I didn't
stay, I point out. I only started to commit myself. I

only investigated the possibility . . . the possibilities. "Myself, two or three times I tried suicide. No, three. But it was a long time ago. Gas the first time. My lungs were sick for a month. I was seventeen. It was after the accident (she broke all her toes tobogganing). I tell her how I couldn't decide on the method. And now? she asks. Now I want to go back. I miss my kids. I'm angry at letting her have the beach place for the whole summer. Why should she be having fun when I'm not? And how do you know she doesn't suffer? I don't. But I hope she suffers at least 10 per cent of what I suffer. Would you take her back if she excused herself? Do you hate her? No, yes.

She says she never hated anyone. "You know, I never talk with your brother like this, the way we talk now." It is light almost. My head is swollen and spinning. I sleep in one of the sixteen beds.

I am up at eight, don't get out of bed till nine. Getting out of bed has been difficult, a major obstacle. I vacillate. I sweat. Turn from side to side, lying there awake for hours sometimes. The dog is restless, woofing under his breath at cowbells. I think about how I played ball with Tommy on the beach the day I left. He was clouting a beach ball with an old piece of bamboo. He loved hitting the ball on the roof so I would have to climb up for it.

Outside, Sandy attacks the cows, chasing them across the field. There isn't a soul in sight as I unzip to pee, but just at that moment a roar—two jets scream past at a hundred feet. The Swiss Air Force on maneuvers.

"Please stay," she begs at breakfast. "What are you gaining by going back now. Stay. Rest. You have waited this long. We will . . ." She makes promises of fun. I am weakest in the morning. I dread going back. But here they wait on me hand and foot. It's so unrealistic. I have to start doing by myself, somehow. Living alone. I think about the shock of going back to New York from this sleepy place and then I don't think about it. It just gets me scared to think about it. She sees my face. She pours me more coffee, marmalades my bread. Temptress.

In Lausanne we go to a travel agent next to the railway station. I make a reservation for Montreal. At the end of the day I call up and cancel it. Then the next day I make the reservation again. They argue with me. They plead. All I can tell them is that I don't really want to go back, but I must.

My brother and I sit down with a pen and paper and make a list of my problems. Block them out. The apartment. A residence hotel. The movers. The car (sell it). The dogs. The California job. The bank accounts. We list everything: where to get my mail, cancel her charge accounts, insurance, changing wills, cashier's checks, a good storage company.

Block your problems out, he advises; it's the only
way. "Think of your son. Set him an example. You
want her to win everything? Nothing could make
her happier. Is that what you want? Recoup your
losses. You lost a couple of rounds, now start winning
some." (I see only further losses.) "You'll try?" he
wants to know. I can't assure him. I know what
feels impossible inside me; he doesn't. A month ago
I was asked, "Can you go any lower?" See? It's always possible. I don't know how to go about climbing out. I don't know if I want to. Thoughts of what
awaits me in New York launches panic. "Make
plans," he advises me. Like what? For what? To go
where? "Do you want her to win everything? To take
it all? Where is your self-respect? Where is your—?"
I forget. I really don't remember. The dog comes
over and puts his head on my lap. "And remember,
you've got to get your sleep."

"You've gained weight here," says Arlette.
"You must have more energy, no? You do feel
somewhat better, don't you?" asks Ben.
While they talk my mind wanders. I dwell on the
same subjects over and over: the apartment in New
York where I can't spend five minutes alone, the
New York shrink I ran out on, the lawyers, all that
dirty laundry. Escape. Flee. I'm a specialist. How
can I go back? How can I stay here?
"I'm going to be blunt with you. You're riddled
with guilt. Self-pity. That's why you can't function."

I stare at him. "Let's run through it again. When
you get back to New York what's the first thing
you're going to do?" I draw a blank. "The very first
thing? You can't remember?" I shake my head.
"Look, stay here. Or go for a week and take care of
things and come right back. You can stay as long as
you want till you're better. Two months, six months,
a year. Invest, he advises. Make a Swiss corporation.
A Liechtenstein corporation. Stay two more days.
Why do you want to go to Montreal on the way
back?

"Do you have any sex drive?" he asks. "Have some
more wine. The easiest thing is to let yourself go. Do
you want to sit someplace and look catatonic like
that forever?" (The idea seems attractive somehow.)
"Because that's where you're headed. Fight her. Get
the kids. You can live anywhere. You can do it. I
know you. I know you can do it." ("He used to be
jealous of your having children. He used to envy your
bohemian life," she had confided at the farm.)

Just because someone tells me what I should do
doesn't mean I can do it. And besides, who knows if
he is right. Just because I can't make judgments for
myself. Just because I have no habits, feel nothing,
no values, no love, no care, no home, no work, no
personality—well, that doesn't mean everything, does
it? I'm superman. I can get along without all that,
right? Who's crazy? I run to people, to talk, for advice, to tell them my tale of anguish, for company.

These days I can no more laugh than a turtle can
fly I can no more do what he bids than—I *can't:* my
theme song.

She drives me to the airport at Geneva.

At Paris, where I change, the Air Canada flight
to Montreal is three hours late. What am I going to
do in the next three hours? I guess I am going to
spend it sitting alone. It occurs to me that in twelve
days in Switzerland I managed not to spend three
hours alone at any time the whole time I was there.

II

from notebook two

July 25.

Knickerbocker, a beer. Hospital. Where I woke up to see a 5 per cent dextrose solution dripping into my right arm. My left arm tied to the bedpost. Mangled the left wrist with a long knife, cutting all kinds of important threads except the one I was aiming for. Failed at that so swallowed pills, almost everything in the medicine chest and then turned on gas in the kitchen and closed all windows and doors. Super smelled it fourteen hours later. I missed Friday completely. They got back from the moon that day. Friday, I am told, friends calling up. Phone ringing. I am there unconscious on the kitchen floor. My time wasn't up. I had left notes, key names and addresses. They all came running to the hospital. Married friends and unmarried, parents, squirrels from the park, solid types, lawyers, kangaroos, psychoanalysts. Some combination of them got me transferred out of Knickerbocker (they had tied my legs too) and over to Winston, where, weirdly, my daughter was born a little over a year ago.

They have this top floor place, with wall-to-wall carpeting, formica and motel coloring. Tower 9. For loonies. I don't even have a sense of feeling close to death, although I am told I was in the emergency room for an hour or two. I don't remember a sense of death. Not a sniff of it. I just went to sleep. On the kitchen linoleum. With a pillow under my head. And when I woke up with a pillow, in the hospital, all I could think was "Oh shit" and I wasn't the least grateful.

Who am I writing this to? That's always the problem. It's not like a letter. Why am I writing this? Who is the addressee?

I still feel languishing and non-functioning.

Although I am not dead I still feel dead just like I felt dead before I tried to make myself really dead. Inert. Not alive. Empty. Without sense. That I could burn my fingers with matches and not feel anything. That I could pull my hair from my head and beard as I had done and not feel any pain.

All I did was make the marks of my suffering physical and visible for the world to see. Not enough to pull out my hairs one by one and pluck my beard and hide money and not do the dishes and be immune to the stink of my body. Not enough never to do the laundry, to panic outside laundromats. Not to sleep for six months.

Before falling unconscious, drunk, pain at my wrist, blood on my clothes. Remember a bucket filled with blood and vomit, a bucket my wife used to mop the kitchen floor with. Recall nothing from being unconscious, no dreams, no other worlds. Just void. Nothing. Blank. Cessation. Shit! The people I've hurt, the people I've worried.

Just had lunch. Lime Jell-O. Which was the only thing I remember eating at Knickerbocker.

This is the week of the moon guys coming back and the Ted Kennedy business with that girl drowned in his car. Where do I fit into that? I don't, any more than anyone else. Who am I writing this to? Let's say myself. Period. So anything goes. And the hell with the style.

Some dreams I had the last two nights:

Coming back to the apartment and finding it re-furnished with the walls barer and a different color, the bookcases down, oriental throw rugs scattered about. Paula there, hanging paintings and murals and psychedelia, saying to her mother, "That's David's favorite." David? I am mortified, terrified. I look for my place but I don't find it. Right under my nose she pulled a fast one.

The next night I was traveling with a lot of people. Friends. Not Paula. I had my son along. It was London. I would think I had lost track of his whereabouts from time to time. We had a kind of three-room suite. There were walks to restaurants and trips to the sea, not in London, but somewhere nearby. Sometimes I would go to the sea on horseback. Then I left the horse somewhere and forgot about it. While looking for the horse, at one point I passed a clothing shop which had some nice clothes in it but I didn't buy anything.

Coming back from the moon. What did that have to do with all this? Nobody's ever been there before and I've never tried to kill myself before. There has been all this lunacy, even in sending people to the moon when people like me are still trying to kill themselves right here. And rain since I've been here, plenty of rain. Better than the sun in a place like this.

It's Dr. Kim now. I somehow drew a Korean resident. A little fellow. He is difficult to understand. His English. He's from Seoul. He's well-read and talks to me superficially about Katherine Anne Porter, Tolstoy, Hemingway and Thomas Mann. He seemed a little offended when I told him I wanted a private doctor upstairs. In Tower 10. This being Tower 9.

This morning they had a meeting of the patients and the staff in which the staff outnumbered the pa-

tients two to one. Arlene Silver, this aggressive-
sounding babe, complained about the food. Another
girl, Linda something, complained of having to go to
sleep too early. Then an old man said he wasn't
being helped here, that he had no mental problem
but a lung congestion problem, that he was seventy-
one (he looks ninety-one), that he was weak, that
his bowels weren't functioning right. Arlene Silver
didn't like that about Mr. Loeb's bowels. She said
she is sick to death of hearing him complain about
his bowels. Then she griped about Mr. Rosenberg's
television-watching habits and the way he domi-
nated the dayroom which also had a phonograph in it
that she liked to hear. Then Queenie, a sullen black
girl, said this was all ridiculous. Dr. Pine agreed.
He's about thirty-five. I said everyone in here and
including myself seemed in a lethargic funk. From
inactivity. The mopey faces being dragged around
this place. I am scared of disintegrating further, of
slipping into a complete nothing state. They make
you make your own bed and serve food every other
day or so. I feel as sluggish as I did in Switzerland.
In Montreal I was forced to do some stuff. Not much.
And in New York. I didn't function well in New
York, alone, but I knew where to mooch meals. I
got good at it. Christ, I shouldn't have done it. It
really closed a lot of doors. It finished that movie,
screwed up my left hand, a financial mess, took me
out of circulation, powdered my brain.

My roommates.

Roger Levine, Jewish, twenty-three, Harvard, Phi Beta Kappa, spent a year in Tanzania learning Swahili and painting and reading Jung and having an affair with a Swedish woman with three children. He came to a stop in New York six weeks after a bad acid trip and well into masturbation and crazy abstract paintings and mother-fucking fantasies and making-himself-pregnant fantasies. He's on heavy tranquilizers but yesterday he flipped out screaming at an attendant. They sedated him with a shot and put him in the "quiet room" for the night. He's a pretty good artist.

Harris, an eighteen-year-old Brandeis High School black Puerto Rican. He has some problem, sexual it seems, that he won't specify to me or his doctor. He seems indifferent, sleepy, and suicidal but he doesn't want to ruin his pretty body with anything messy. He likes to act and wants to be an actor. He can draw. He writes poetry. Once he wrote eighty pages of a novel. He is handsome and not talkative unless you are alone with him. Then he becomes romantic, philosophical, confessional. "A month ago I was about to make love to this girl on my mother's bed when my mother come in. She was very angry."

Mr. Rosenberg, who was in Japan a year and a half ago, and who is sixty, a television-watcher, a horse-race follower, a movie projectionist, who smokes two packs of cigarettes a day and doesn't be-

lieve in the scare talk about cancer, except that he
coughs all night long in his sleep.

The others are Mrs. Pine (no relation to the
Tower 9 boss), who is about sixty-five and lost her
husband earlier this year and moans "Oh, oh, oh,
someone help me, please help me" on and off all day;
Judy, nineteen years old, Catholic, who slashed her
wrists and her right breast (the tape protrudes from
her dress)—she has asked me several times, "Do you
know what I should do?"; Chic, twenty-three, a fag,
who took four hundred libriums in a week and says,
"When I go out on passes suicide is the first thing I
think of"; Linda, twenty-one, her husband a dealer,
she taking junk with him for three years, an epilep-
tic, three times before in hospitals; Arlene, forty-five
and acting eighteen, good-natured and pleasant and
euphoria is her problem, she says; Mrs. Reid, sixty,
puffy, red-faced and always chain-smoking Pall
Malls.

What is the schedule of steps? How do I get from
A to B? Who is going to help me? I'm told that I
have to do it myself but I need direction. Won't
somebody direct me? I know that inside it's only a
matter of degree between me and Mrs. Pine strolling
endlessly back and forth, moaning, "Oh help me,
help me. Somebody listen." I am that way inside.

How can I stop this drifting? By confessing everything I am and know for ten hours a day? I want

to get my left wrist working. My thumb dangles use-
lessly the way it is now.

Dr. Kim says he'll ask Dr. Pine about getting me
a private doctor. If I can get a good doctor then
I'm on my way, but if not I'm sunk. I can't repeat
all my shit to a third one and then maybe a fourth.
But if he's good I'm moving on again, and out,
dealing with Paula, the kids, the lawyers, the money,
the apartment, the work, the embarrassment, the
lies. I've done this and suffered that. How much
more? Isn't it enough?

Try making a list of my lies, my failures, my ac-
complishments.

—Sticking around through the spring while Paula
went out with her diaphragm.

—Letting her change to those grain foods the way
she did and using the drugs and not protesting, not
fighting her every inch of the way.

—Letting myself run down into a state of dejec-
tion and despondency over her behavior and my own
inability to regain control.

—Letting her breakdown break me down, letting
her illness tear me apart, sitting by and watching it
all, impotent to stop it.

—Hoping for a miracle.

—Going without sex (because of despondency?
self-punishment? loss of self-confidence?).

—Allowing her to spend money for Mrs. B., the
baby-sitter lady, for clothes, for records, for macro-

biotic food. You could have said: not with *my* money
you don't. Yet you didn't. Fool!

—Becoming a suffering prisoner of the circumstances, buffeted, stunned, smashed down day after
day.

Was my past all a lie? Did I limp through these
nine years only with her help? If so, then what am I
without her?

I wrote five books and hundreds of articles and
stories and all the while she was there, feeding, encouraging, protecting, supporting, maternalizing,
loving, demanding love back, starting and dropping
diets. This is *so* painful.

Can I even write without her?

Yes, goddamit. I can. I must. I will.

Last night Martin came first, with a tale of Frank
Elliott bringing regards from T.A. at college and
how proud they all are of me up there. Then Hoyle
appeared and asked how long are you going to be
here, you don't look crazy, and he looked uncomfortable; then Saul, double-breasted blazered, with a
story of a relative in Chicago who is confined for
three months every time she tries it ("Who says
you *shouldn't* be upset when your wife flips out and
pulls out like that?"); then Sam and Hilda, having

gotten their sofa into the new apartment and Sam
having shot some movie in Harlem today; and then
Brigit, up in the solarium after Ping-Pong, unan-
nounced, instead of her husband; and then my
mother and father, and then Dr. Alexandrovitch.

I told her that being outside briefly today (my
father insisted on my going and changing bank accounts so Paula doesn't get her hands on my money)
was like seeing how the barrier, this hospital, that
shielded me was artificial and that the whole clang-
ing, banging business goes on while I've come to a
stop.

"Once I went back to Vienna after the war to look
at my street, the house where I grew up. I remember feeling the same thing when I looked at this little
rose pattern border that went up the staircase. I always used to watch it when I climbed the stairs as
a little girl. Ten or fifteen years had passed but those
faded roses I had looked at, climbing the stairs as a
child, they were still right there."

I sometimes feel I let her down. She's probably a
good shrink—for someone else. That she tried, but
she failed with me.

"Did you really want to die?" she asks. "Or was it
a cry for help?"

I thought. I said, Who knows? When I woke up
and saw the mangled mess from the knife I took pills
and sealed myself in the kitchen with the gas. "It
could have worked," I told her. I explained the L-

shaped kitchen. The neighbor told the super he smelled gas, but what about if the neighbor was away? I don't know. I told her that when I woke up in Knickerbocker I thought, "Shit, I'm still here." Except as I talked to her in that little air-conditioned back staff office (bottles and rolls of tape everywhere) I felt angry at myself, maybe for the first time, at what I had done.

She seemed pleased. She was perhaps less formal than I had ever seen her. She's very intellectual, very cerebral. Very much a lady. She went away. I had spent three months with her getting nowhere with her telling me Paula was sick and had to be treated accordingly. I spent the three lowest months of my life three times a week with her and got nowhere, except to attack myself.

My new lot is to work with a private doctor upstairs, a Dr. Nathanson. I'm scared. Paula comes home from the beach today (July 31). My father returned to Florida to see about getting their stuff shipped back to New York. He and my mother went down there to find a condominium to which to retire. I fucked up their plans. With Paula back he is no longer free to romp up to my apartment and collect my papers and personal effects. When they let me out to go up to the apartment and the bank with him that day, it was an agony, a return to a nightmare.

Martin: "Elliott says you should go and get drunk for two weeks, puke your guts out and then start again, and keep doing it until you're out of it. . . . Elliott says he heard of a guy who jumped from the Empire State Building and landed three floors down on a wide ledge with broken legs, but before they could get down to him he crawled over to the edge and went over. *That's* determination."

A bad, hot sleepless night. The first day of sun after eleven days of rain. Here, I would rather have rain. I crawled around on drenched sheets all night. I had a crazy dream, and with the same ingredient as the last three nights—approaching sex, erection, lust—then nothing happens. The dream this time: a trip to Israel. En route to the Feldmans I bawled Paula out and told her we were through. That I wouldn't stand for her shit. (Earlier in the real day, Danny had said, "We misinterpreted it. We all thought you and Paula simply wanted to separate, and that *she* was the crazy one.") Before arriving at the Feldmans' house in Jerusalem I stop, alone, at a favorite cafe, doing research on my travel guide. I chatted with the boss. Then I went out to buy a couple of things and it was night. I was walking. I

had a kite for Tom. I thought I needed a rest. I lay
down to sleep. The Feldmans found me asleep by the
side of the road. I got in their car. Aaron was there,
and not very friendly, unusual for him. He must
have heard something. And so was Yakov, his
second-born. We got back to their house and found
Margaret Carr, Paula's shrink, summoning me into
the next room. She finally wanted to talk to me.
"You ruined my marriage," I said. "You didn't try
to show Paula how to live with me." "That's non-
sense," she said. "Let's talk in a little while. Wait
in the next room." The other room was a small
auditorium, right in the Feldmans' apartment in
Jerusalem. I was ready to take on Margaret Carr. I
had made up my mind about Paula. I waited. I had
a drink. I met a girl, someone similar to one of the
kindly nurses here. We started to make it, her on
top. But it didn't culminate. "I didn't bring my diaphragm," the girl said. "Well, okay. . . ." And
then the auditorium filled and Margaret presided
over a discussion of politics and sociology and urban
problems. I waited and waited to see Margaret Carr
alone. I noticed as she lectured that she had a
withered left hand. I kept waiting. The whole discussion was beside the point. I couldn't have cared
less. Let's finally get at the truth. Let's finally hear
it. After her talk I burst into her office. Margaret
Carr was with two men. She looked tired, had her

feet up. One of the men was Frank Eisnitz, a kid
last seen in a junior high school class. Once I had
seen his yellow-stained underpants. Another time I
had seen him deliver a talk in the auditorium on
building his own radio. Margaret said I had to wait.
And the dream ended, frustrated, without an answer. I never had my talk with Margaret.

My mother, on why they came back to New York
from Florida so abruptly: "I told my friend, 'Oh, it
was a little nervous breakdown Jesse had.'"

I played Ping-Pong with Roger last night and
really felt good. . . . Dr. Kim: "I think maybe you
only work an hour or two a day. Don't read too much.
Bowl, paint, participate in the activities, eh? I think
so. . . ."

Dr. A. reminded me that I once had a dream of
choking Paula, I was that furious with her. The
dream was long ago, that weekend in the spring
when we went to her home town in Pennsylvania
together, when she got stoned the moment we arrived and took off in the car and went into all the
drugstores in town and tried to buy a diaphragm.
She came back to the house giggling and laughing:

"Oh well, I just wanted to see the scenes at the different drugstores. . . ."

I am safe here. But when the pay phone is out of order, which is often, I panic.

A young neurologist-intern, Dr. Clark on his button, looked at my left hand and pricked it with a pin and asked me to open and close and such, and he said it looked like it was healing well by itself. He set up an appointment for me at the hand clinic for next Tuesday. God. Another problem. I can't even bear to think about it. "We've got some of the best hand men in the country here. They'll evaluate it. I think you'll get back full or almost full use."

The room lets in a lot of noise. It faces south, to the Empire State Building on the left, the Hotel Manhattan, the McGraw-Hill Building. Traffic roars down below all day. Diesels and screaming trucks. The Hotel Henry Hudson is across the street. A Finast down below. Sirens wail. Black smoke from three chimneys. How peaceful, how calming. At night it roars on.

My reading matter. *The Tanks of Tammuz*, by Shabtai Teveth; *Journal of a Novel*, by John Steinbeck; *The Border* and *A Young Man in the Know*, by Regis Debray; and *Cowboys Don't Cry*, by L. J. Davis.

Gary came back to visit yet again. Why does he keep coming? I hardly know the guy. Messages of good will. Get back together. All you have to do is want her. Period. Presto. Magic. But I don't want her, Gary. Leave me alone. I'm not sure there still isn't a hint, a small possibility of some kind, he says. I'm pretty sure, Gary, even if you're not. Guilty about how he treated his wife two years ago when he left her in pregnancy and took up with a macrobiotic chick, then returned to his wife and to make up to her got her pregnant again. He should be in this place too. He's crazier than me.

Arlette arrives, via Swissair, feeling she failed me. She spoke to Levi. "How could he—when he was so concerned about his children?" She said I was selfish. (I lost self-respect, myself, ego—it's not a question of selfishness—couldn't her Levi have told her that?) Levi thinks you must have taken "something" to precipitate it. True enough. Then Saul comes— the fourth time—with news that he had his old job back but also that he found two theses similar to the one he was planning on Emerson-Thoreau-Whitman. (Brigit calls to say she found an apartment for me. I'm not interested.) Last night Cal came over with a pint of Irish whiskey. He spent a couple of weeks at his farm. Wouldn't tell a soul, he swears.

Lots of people break up and get hurt, he says. He also found me an apartment. He is looking very good, tanned and in new clothes. ("I called Bellevue first, then here. I got a lot of weird friends. I've tracked people down before.") Rozanne was inside, gum-crackling cousin Rozanne, from Scarsdale, unseen in six years or so, with two little boys, five and nine, in analysis, and she says she wants to meet Cal. ("I just *knew* he was Scandinavian," she says.) What the fuck is she doing here? Why after six years of unfriendliness does she pick *now* to come visit? She is going through some kind of separation from her husband Jack. He has taken an apartment in the city. Then Elaine comes, my agent. "Listen," she says, "those movie guys won't take no for an answer. They're willing to wait until you get better. They've been told you were in a car accident." Tell them I was really badly smashed up, that the first reports didn't reflect the seriousness of it all. Let me alone! Make the damn movie without me. Hire some hack. Then Cal leaves and Rozanne goes on about how her oldest kid reacted to analysis when he was four years old, showing the shrink his bloody fingernails and saying, "Help." And then how her younger kid, Billy, gets along very well with his analyst. ("His analyst always says to me everything's just fine when I come pick him up—but listen, I mean, at forty dollars an hour, I don't think that's any kind of answer") and Arlette, sitting back, tired, feeling it's two o'clock in the morning, Swiss time. "How can you feel better here?" she asked me. "Are you angry at yourself? Will you try it again? Your whole mess is still out there, isn't it? Everything you were afraid of." She needed a dentist and I gave her the name of mine before she left, but since she's staying at my parents' house she wound up going to their dentist in New Jersey.

Brigit: "Oh, you're not crazy, you're not a mental case. Get *out* of that place."

Elaine: "You seem fine talking to me. It's just when you're alone that it starts. I sometimes feel that way in the office."

Yesterday I met Dr. Nathanson for the first time. He is tall and hefty. The private doctor. I told him facts and stories. He just listened to it all. At the end he asked me how I felt about being in the hospital.

I ought to get my manuscript. Externalize the anger. What direction? Constructive things. A burnt-out case I? Avoiding the finality of my situation. How I exclaimed my helplessness. I felt helpless. Feel helpless. Tommy at the beach: "Jerry can throw higher than you. He can run faster than you, too." (Jerry, his mother's boyfriend.)

Went to see *Putney Swope*. An odd quartet. Led by a twenty-two-year-old big-bosomed Miss Goldstein, nursing assistant from Mount Vernon, Barnard student. And me, bearded, and sixty-year-old Mrs.

Pine moaning "Oh, oh, oh" in the back of the
theater, and Arlene, pointing out on the way over,
that she lived on Central Park South. I got nervous
at the movie. I got nervous just being out on the
street. It's a good thing I was shepherded.

Arlette: You don't trust yourself.

That's one way of putting it.

Now then: recovering from self-inflicted wounds
at Winston Hospital, the author.

Dr. Kim: And some day you may forgive yourself.

Dr. Nathanson: "You made your own nine-to-five
routine. (Am I habitual, inflexible?)

My physical ailments: the thin-picked beard; the
dancing black spot before my left eye following my
vision from left to right (it started when I woke at
Knickerbocker, possibly the oxygen deprivation or
something); a pain in the right side of my head and
jaw as though from a blow or fall; a hurting cavity
in my upper right fang; my butchered left wrist;
burning when I piss from the catheter they stuck in
at Knickerbocker; mysteriously bruised loins; bowels in a continuing mess; painful callus on the bottom of my left foot. And general fuzziness of the
brain, inability to read and concentrate. There's too
much to start repairing.

Arlette brought down three copies of my manuscript. Very strange to read it now. It seems so out
of the past.

Why is this notebook getting more disjointed and

fragmented? My head should be getting together, not coming apart even more.

Reading that manuscript took me back to what I was doing when I wrote it. It forecasted so many things. Maybe it's the first of the things I don't want to do that must be done. Must?

Taking a shower, I keep my bandaged wrist outside the shower curtain.

Arlette: Do you still feel hate for Paula? Do you? You really do?

Yesterday, the visitors fell off. Just Arlette came. They've all come once, or twice, had their look, got bored.

I found this in last year's manuscript:

Some people know what to do and are able to do it. Some people know what to do but are unable to do it. Some people don't know what to do and their hang-ups will keep them from ever finding out.

Roger seems better. Talks more, paints more, goes out more on passes. Last night a sick discussion with Arlene, Chic and Linda about suicide, their many attempts and methods. Oh God, let my hand improve. Sometimes I feel like there is a fog around my head, a sticky, mucousy fog.

Why don't my parents get upset when they come to visit? Why don't they show something? Some remorse, some venom. I tell my father I was fucking people when Paula was pregnant, and I tell my mother too, and he says so long as you were a son of a bitch once (or did he say *bastard?*) doesn't mean you'll always be one. I even discussed why he sent me to Hebrew School so long. Everyone did it. If it wasn't for your brother's rotten attitude toward it, he says, you would have liked it more. You followed him in everything he did. She files her nails, brings me down some mail. He goes through my bank statements at home and brings me a report. Arlette says my parents are adorable. I say I've slipped back to his silent, inexpressive way of dealing with things. I don't feel I've ever learned anything positive from him.

Dr. Nathanson: "How do you feel about your father telling you you didn't have an identity of your own, that you just copied your brother?"

I am stumped for an answer.

Are they my emotional antecedents? If so, then where are their emotions? I seem to have overlooked something all my life. Who am I? is such an adolescent question. I'll never learn it, or I don't like what I learn, so I learn and then I'm angry at

myself for being so cold inside for so long. What am
I doing to prevent what happened from happening
again? (In the spring, Dr. A.: "You talk as though
you have no freedom, a prisoner.") I don't like
the prison I made for myself. There are plenty of
prisons out there; why go to the trouble of building
one for yourself.

Did Paula feel good about my trying to take my
life? I remember all the hints she made about suicide, about a music teacher of hers that did it in
1957, about how my cousin tried it, suggestions like
that to me in the spring, encouragement. No. She
probably believes that people look on her as the
cause of it, that so many people knew she had
cracked up months ago and that I was wearing down
trying to hold on and keep her together and keep the
kids together.

No dream last night. Something about a horse.
Nothing that stayed. Sleeplessness is so chronic. Five
or six hours' sleep, even with the pill they gave me
here at ten o'clock, and then I'm up at five o'clock,
sweating and tossing on wet wrinkled sheets.

Nathanson: "Whatever prevented you from taking steps at home, in the service, and in school, is
the same thing that prevents you *now.*"

Why did I do that business during her pregnancy?
asks Nathanson.

"Who suggests you stay with your parents when
you get out of here?" (Nathanson)

"You would rather suffer the situation than leave it." (Nathanson)

"She was certainly sending you messages." (Nathanson)

(Paula, in the spring, to Dr. A.: "I long ago ceded my mind over to him. Now I am getting it back.")

Saul's visit:

"But weren't you the same person last month that you were two years and ten years ago, having now to deal with latent fears you had then but didn't have to deal with?"

Saul: "You could maimed yourself worse. Much worse. When I was at Kings County Hospital people came in there really maimed, crippled." He left medical school after two years, became an academic—American studies.

Saul: "It's like you'll be twenty-one or twenty-two again, out loose, on the make." I wouldn't want to be twenty-one or twenty-two again, but then have I ever stopped being twenty-one or twenty-two? The only thing worse is being fourteen. But have I ever stopped being fourteen? Who the fuck knows? All the time I was married I was mentally unfaithful, even though there weren't many other girls really. Saul looks down at this confession. His experience is different. I was loved, but I didn't love in return. I had a great thing and I blew it. Saul: "You didn't have such a great thing. Paula always was kind of whacked out, long before you knew her, too."

Neurosis is the inability to love, I just read.
Then what is hell?
Hell is the inability to love: Father Zossima.
Don't fuck around with it: that's the truth.
The more I look into myself, the bigger is the mess
I see there. But does that make me different from
anyone else?

I used to sit in Dr. A.'s office and say nothing for
weeks on end. She'd say, "It's like you were born yesterday and have no history." She'd also say, "Somebody must have treated you the same way you treat
other people." Did it all start when I was a new-
born and my mother had female trouble and the doctor told her not to lift me? If it started back then,
then what can I do about it? Isn't it hopeless? What
do you do now about not being held enough as an
infant? Be held by a shrink for the rest of your life?
Running to so many different people with my tale
of anguish, as though it were all Paula's fault. It's
her fault insofar as she stopped dealing with me and
started in dealing with herself. Mr. Schwartz, West
Side Realty: "You look so unhappy. Go to a rabbi
with her. Try it." Chic: "I've been here three weeks.
I haven't been helped at all." Roger: "If I'd have
found myself with a Korean doctor here that would
have been the last straw. It's Kafka come true."
Childhood ends, finally. Dependency ends.

Nathanson yesterday (August 5) asked about a program of discharge. I sidestepped it and we talked of . . . what? I don't remember.

Cathy Waller, twenty-one or twenty-two, nursing assistant, smiley and shapely and available, yesterday, after the sensitivity exercises, pressed me and pressed me: "How did you feel? Did you love her? Why did you do that?" I kept saying, "I don't know," over and over. It made me wonder if I ever showed genuine feelings. About the pregnancy thing, with my Aunt Sophie, nursing: "Are you sure it didn't disgust you?" The room smelled sour is all I remember, and her lying sideways on the bed. Did you ever remember any of that when your wife nursed? Any feelings about it? . . . Do you mean feelings about it *then* or *now?* . . . Either way. . . . No. None. I don't remember.

Feel funny having Cathy press me. She was a child, twelve or thirteen or fourteen or so when I got married. But I can talk to her, easier maybe than to Nathanson. You give yourself all these multiple-choice answers, she says. You say maybe it was this, or that, or that. But which is it really? How did you really feel? Did you love her, your wife? Do you love Tommy? Did you love your parents? Did you love yourself? Did you ever love any woman?

Bud calls from Montreal: "You're here and if it wasn't that someone found you, you'd have died. So it's like you've died and you're reborn. It's a second life."

To have worked at my books, the way I worked, meant shutting out my environment, and people, partially and totally, and doing the same thing I did at home as a child when I would close the door to my bedroom and draw pictures for hours.

Cathy Waller: "Why is it easier for you to love a dog? You don't have to get involved. What will people see?" They will see all my deficiencies.

Press me Dr. Nathanson, press me! I'm pulling on my beard again. I must not pull on my beard. I must not pull on my beard. Dormant, moping, lulling.

Was I ever lavish? Was I ever honest? I am pulling on my beard right this second.

I'm thirty-three, for Christ's sake. Thirty-three! Is there anything else left? Or have I shot my wad?

Cathy: Does it mean if you find you have a heart that you won't be able to write any more? Now that doesn't make sense, does it?

I tried to commit suicide because: Paula found me inadequate and looked elsewhere; I wasn't able to work and didn't want to and wanted to fail; I wasn't able to decide and value things on my own, apartment, feeding myself, what clothes to wear, and the little decisions were maddening; my appearance in the mirror seemed disfigured; I lost my children; my future seemed empty; my will power and ambition got lost; my sexual drive disappeared; I fell back on my father; I was a burden on my friends; I stopped making plans. I wanted to forget everything; everything was too painful and too much to cope with, too overwhelming. The waves running over me got bigger and bigger and finally I went under. But I was washed ashore and given artificial respiration.

But isn't it all still true? And with added complications now?

It's too *noisy* here.

How did I write those books? How? What did I have to say? How was I able to read?

What is my treatment here? Is it novel, old-fashioned, or what? My room has four red chairs, four studio beds with green coverings, four desks at four windows, two closets. In occupational therapy a German girl looks at my pastel and crayon drawings. They don't seem like much to me, but she finds a lot in them. They're abstractions.

I'm starting to pace the halls, from the OT room to the dayroom, looking in all the rooms as I pass. And old Mr. Loeb sits out in front of my room reading the *Reader's Digest* and trying to strike up a conversation every time I wander past.

It's better to have a breakdown younger than older.

Nathanson, today, making me scramble:

"You see therapy as laceration?"

"Was there ever a catchall guide to the per-
plexed?"

"You want improvement so quickly. One way or
another you've been like this all your life. You want
a miracle."

"Am I supposed to do the work for you?"

For some reason I told Nathanson all the women
I ever made it with, starting with Rita and ending
with Mary in the spring. I forgot two names. It
didn't seem to add up to anything to me.

Yesterday, at dinner out, Hilda said she'd been
with an analyst for six months before he started com-
municating with her.

If my writing is a defense, a refuge, then what?

Nathanson: "Why didn't you get angry at me for
canceling the appointment yesterday? Why didn't
you get angry at Paula? You were afraid of losing
her. You were afraid that if you'd have gotten angry
at me, you'd have lost me, too."

Martha came to visit today (August 7) and she
recognized Roger Levine from high school in Cleve-
land. "He was a real cool head," she says. "Not many
like him. He used to intimidate a lot of teachers
there." I like Martha a lot. Of the wives of my
friends I like her the most, possibly with the excep-

tion of Hilda. Her . . . something. "Your problem—
I used to think it was just a Wasp problem, com-
municating emotion and feeling your own emotions."

Borrowing my razor every morning from the
nurse's office, and then returning it to them. Why do
I shave around what's left of my beard? Bike riding
in Central Park. Strolling with Miss Goldstein around
Bethesda Fountain.

Paula's visit here. I gave her a check, and a
credit-canceling letter from Bloomingdale's. I told
her I knew how I was to her during her pregnancy with Suzie. She said I should live out of the
city, that I should take this apartment in the Village
that will be one of two swapped for our apartment.
Her voice brought tears. I had to stop talking. I felt
and fought the swelling in my throat, a memory of
a voice that once meant something, a memory of a
person, for my pain, for the magnitude of my actions.
She looked crazy and left me a copy of *The Order
of the Universe*. I gave her the car keys and the reg-
istration.

Cathy Waller: You expect instant catharsis. Your
grief when she visited you: isn't grief appropriate?

Why do people cry at funerals? You have feelings.
Why be surprised? So you showed emotions. Do you
think we're holding out on you? We don't have the
truth serum you keep asking for. You don't trust
people, do you? So your father doesn't show emotions: so what? People care about you. I do, Dr.
Nathanson does, Paula, your father, friends.

Roger: Ethically, you did the right thing. With
your pent-up anger you physically abused yourself.
Your alternative was murdering your wife.

I thought of it many times.

I described for Cathy my first meeting with Paula,
the first date when I took her to that restaurant
and told her dozens of dirty jokes. (Why were you
kidding yourself? Why were you pulling the wool
over her eyes? You were sure no one could love you
for what you were.) I described the original Paula
I had known before soiling her with my trashy
handling. How she was talkative, funny, effusive,
bubbly, laughing. The things we did together.

Roger has been drawing and painting daily since
he's been here. He has a kind of record, in line and
color, of his condition since he's been here.

My father comes again, with clean laundry. He
says my work was the only thing that was important.
"You felt you and your work were so important

you didn't care how and whether you hurt people."
That's true.

Bob, on his visit: "Don't take so much guilt on
yourself. Paula worshiped you. She thought your
work and leaving you alone to work was the most
important thing in the world. That was *her* hang-up.
She fed your neurosis and you fed hers, too."

Everybody sheds some light on it.

I am thinking about feeling, instead of just feeling. I am thinking about what I feel, instead of
feeling.

A telephone conversation, from the wall phone
outside the nurse's station, with Tommy: "I'm sorry
I can't be with you now, but I love you."

"I have a cat—Bobbiya Lucy. It's Siamese."

III

from notebook three

August 10. Cathy twice got me to cry.

Once when she was pressing me ("Why do you feel that way? How did you feel about that?"), I heard a song on the radio. A Doris Day song from half my life ago. It flashed in: I was listening to it in college, half asleep in my room, nearly dark, sitting in a big chair, winter, late afternoon. I was so lonely then, wondering if there would ever be someone, anyone at all. *When I fall in love, it will be*— And there was someone, and then I lost her, through my own stupidity. What guilt I feel. I used to blame it all on her, and on circumstance, and now I blame it all on myself, on my emotional paralysis. Talking to Cathy, I heard the song, and I remembered the chair I was sitting in (it was red, leatherish) and what Mike's radio looked like. And I started to cry. . . .

And later, with Cathy, I showed her a picture of
Tom and I started to cry again. Not much, but it
was some. And I had begun to think I wasn't capable
of it.

"Did you love her?" she asked me.

"I may have loved the person she was once, but
not recently. I'm just not sure. I don't know."

Did you love her, or just not dislike her? Who did
you really like? Tell me some people you've really
liked. Anyone at all? Did you ever tell her she was
important to you? Did you ever make her feel important to you? Maybe. Perhaps. I don't know. No.
No.

I want to go someplace and cry out SHIT or FUCK
or HELP or just scream till I have no voice left. I
need a rooftop or a riverside. There's something inside begging and bulging like that and it wants to
come out.

I went bowling for the first time in my life today—with five other patients and two staff girls. I
enjoyed it.

Today, August 11, I feel so anxious. I feel overweight. Sluggish. I'm farting. I want something else

to happen here. Enough is not happening. Come on,
Nathanson. Get it out of me. Slip me some truth
serum. I've still got a dam inside. Why the panic
today? The place is getting to me. Roger leaves in
a few days, maybe tomorrow. And then Arlette goes
back. And I'm still here, blocked. Now my parents
know the truth. Endlessly picking over my past. I
apologized to them about everything. I'm a bastard,
I admitted it to them. I have been. But intentionally?
Maliciously?

I am drawing more freely. In Occupational Therapy.

Children: the pain of disconnection. Two lives.
One close and the other far away.

Accuse parents should, but don't. Can't now.

Do I want to get well, or don't I?

Stuck into self-pity, indecision, self-accusation.

Living with pain and anxiety. Prolonged: Levi. It
wears you down. You burst.

Nathanson: how do you feel about Robert Montgomery? How do you feel about Eisenhower?

How do you feel about being discharged? Afraid.
But restless here. Stuck. I'm postponing again.

Lawyer.

Apartment.

Work.

See people. Friends.

Girls.

Children.

Dentist.

Friday. Robie. Or maybe Cal.

I feel it's important to get out of the hospital evenings.

Group therapy meeting. Feeling the pressure. Eyes lowered. Look people in the eye. Feeling like a freak outside on the street. While everyone else did this or that in early August, Jesse Jacobi spent the month in the psychiatric ward of a hospital.

August 12. Robert Montgomery cast as the hero of my movie. We are on swings in the park, sitting side by side, talking. We discuss changes to the script. I write down some lines. Then we go to a hotel with the script. The door to the hotel room is locked. We try the back door. It is kind of dingy. Robert Montgomery doesn't care for the hotel room. We try another hotel. He calls the studio. We arrive at the other hotel and it is pretty much the same as the first. We never get a chance to sit down and discuss the script.

With Nathanson I avoid all possible interpretations. He leads me on, suggesting Montgomery is my father, my frustration in dealing with him, how we can never talk, suggestions of homosexuality.

My father tells Arlette the following anecdote, which I have never heard: When he was little he would go up to his father when he was reading the newspaper and beg him to talk to him. "What's to talk about?" he'd say, and go on reading his paper.

George once said, seven or eight months ago, that I treated people like objects.

August 14. Wearing a raincoat, carrying a hammer in my pocket, in a train station, scared, looking around. I see Robie, in whites. He has a tennis racket. He asks me why I'm wearing a raincoat in the summer when it's hot and sunny out. We take the train upstairs and go to a hotel. There are two other people in the hotel room. They are smoking grass. I smoke some. The hotel clerk is in the room, behind a counter. A knock on the door. I look through the peephole. There are police. They question us. They question me about my attempted suicide. I say I am Levine, not my real name. I was born Levine, I say.

Nathanson: You feel you committed two wrongs. You feel guilty. And if you are born Levine then you are not you.

Good-bye Cathy Waller, have a good trip with your husband. She is going to England. She has never been out of the country before. How could I have

learned so much from her. I have been to Europe
eight times or ten. I'll miss you. I give her an auto-
graphed copy of my book. I kiss her good-bye. She
gives me a present. What is it? I go to my room to
open it. A box with a mirror in it.

Why do you suppose she gave you that? asks Nathanson.

I don't know.

Do you look in mirrors much?

I don't like what I see.

So why do you suppose she gave you a mirror?

I don't know.

August 15. I am skiing with my brother. Using
rented equipment. A small slope. I went to a small
house nearby to rent something. Inside it was full of
guns—rifles and submachine guns. A small man
with a deformed eye told me where to rent the ski
stuff. I went back to ski some more and realized I
was sliding downhill on tennis sneakers. I went back
to rent ski shoes. A friend arrived with the Indians.

I have loose front teeth all along the bottom row.
They feel like they are about to fall about. They
look long and red. I have a bucktooth appearance
and can hardly talk but I can push them back to
the crooked place even though I am afraid to move
them for they may fall out.

In the third dream that night it was my turn to clear the dogshit from the street. I had a broom but I needed water. A black man gave me some sewage or used water (brown) to do the job. It was on Broadway and 101st Street.

Nathanson: Once I asked you if you dream and then you go on every session deluging me with your dreams. You send me your books in the mail. What about your real life? What are you thinking? What are you feeling?

Nathanson: You've got all the answers.

Nathanson: That weekend in Boston you told me about. When she visited her roommate from college, the one who used to call her a whore. She was insecure about her ability to maintain a relationship. She wanted to prove the girl was wrong—or right all along.

August 20. Left the hospital today.

In the morning, while I packed, they came around with a portable outfit and gave Mrs. Pine shock treatment in her room. The door was open and I looked in. Will it make her stop moaning?

The other patients look at me like I'm something special to be leaving today. Do they know I'm scared? Do they know how little I've learned? How little I've come?

At one o'clock Saul was downstairs in a car—a red convertible. His friend's. A Mustang. His friend is on vacation. His friend is a shrink.

My room at their apartment: the baby's room. They moved the baby into the kids' room. I have a trundle bed and three drawers in a chest. Saul set to work ripping out wires in a closet and installed a telephone in my room. I don't understand how he understands all these different-colored wires.

Then we drove around looking for a desk, supposedly so I would have a place "to work."

Then I went up to see the kids—and Paula. A horrible feeling going back up there. She was supposed to be there but she wasn't. Some kid opened the door. Wearing an Indian headband and a shirt that looked like mine, a puffy Errol Flynn sort of dueling shirt. Mitchell, he said his name was when I came in. He was about twenty. He said he met Paula at White Lake. Out of 300,000 people there last weekend was this ratty-looking kid the best she could find? He didn't look old enough to shave. In the mud up there. Love and good vibrations and he is wearing my shirt. "She's getting Tommy some shoes or something."

Records were strewn everywhere all over three rooms. And books piled in corners, in boxes, under tables. And clothes all over the floor. And pieces of furniture no longer there. Mitchell: What are you doing here? Who are you and what do you want? This is my apartment. I lived here three years. It's my home. I have no other home. The place smelled from brown rice and sweat.

I pretended to look for some papers. Bedrolls and sleeping bags in the corner.

"That looks like a shirt of mine."

Finally I said it.

"Yeah, I . . . it's uh . . ."

The bell rang. Paula and Tommy and Suzie. Suzie's dress was filthy. Tommy and I hugged and hugged and hugged. One kiss for the baby girl. Tommy had on bell-bottoms and no shirt. I brought him some drawings I made in the hospital. Pictures of flying giraffes and a gadget that had a ball in it.

Hadn't I had dreams in the hospital about being in my apartment and finding everything different? Rearranged?

"I didn't know what I had till I lost it," I said to her.

She put her eyes down. She couldn't look at me. We started playing with the ball game in the living room. Tommy kept shooting it behind the piano. I moved the piano. Paula came in to talk.

"The dogs are your responsibility. What are you going to do with them? . . . The car is my father's originally and he gave it to us, if you'll recall. I'm a good driver and I want it and I hope there'll be no

hassle about it. . . . I'm getting you an apartment
in the West Village. Call this girl Vicki. She'll show
it to you. It's her friend's. It's supposed to be very like
a French garret. It's only eighty dollars a month.
You'll have a lot of expenses, right? Vicki's moving
in here, to our place, and she's getting me an apartment in the East Village plus your apartment. We'll
be subletting this place to Vicki. You can have the
Charles Street apartment starting—"

"Too fast. I just got out of the hospital today."

"No, no. Here. Sit down. Take my hands. It'll be
all right. Oh you should have been in Woodstock.
You should have seen the love. *I took off my shirt.
Me!* I didn't care if everyone saw my little titties.
Don't worry about moving. I'll get people to help
you move. Get out of the city. There are beautiful
people around to help you. Go to the country. Sleep
outdoors. I'm going to travel. I'm going back to the
mountains. I'm going to Florida. Dig it, I'm sleeping
outside. There are beautiful, groovy people around
to talk with up there, up in White Lake. I *left my
tent up there! My tent!* Come on up. You should
come up. We'll talk. I'll introduce you. I can't sleep
with you, but I'll talk. I'll help. I want to help. We'll
live crosstown. *You can bicycle over and see the kids
whenever you want. You know what that means?*
Your children need you. You can see them as much
as you want. Three times a week even. I won't have
a phone. You won't have to make appointments.

There was a guy up in Woodstock who did good things for your son's head."

Outside with Tommy to the park. We read the two books I brought him. We played with the ball toy. ("You hold it and I'll throw it. . . . Now I'll hold it and you throw it. . . . Don't shoot it into the tall grass. . . . Who was in the car when you and Paula were driving? I love you and I missed you. I love you too. Why were you in the hospital?")

We walked. It was seven thirty.

"Let's see if the kite is still there," he suggested.

The kite was one that Paula had given me for my birthday two years ago. A big yellow and red bird. On its first flight it got stuck in the trees. A stuck that wouldn't unstick. Whenever we were in the park we would look to see if it was still there. It was always there; through two years of rain and snow it stayed in the top branches, shredding. As of a few months ago, only a little piece of rag remained.

"I don't think it's still there," I said.

"But can't we look?"

At first we didn't see anything. Finally, finally, it's gone. No. There. *Yes!* A tiny red triangle remained. "Look!" Tommy's eyes following my pointing finger. A brightness. "I see it!"

We walked home, hand in hand. At the traffic light where we waited I cupped his hand in mine and pressed him against my thigh.

At home, Suzie was sleeping. Mitchell was silent.

I called Saul. I'll be back in an hour, for dinner. "No, no," cried Paula. "Stay for dinner. I'm making something good." Well—

In the kitchen Paula cooking buckwheat noodles and squash.

"I'm not finished having babies. I expect to have more. . . . I may see another shrink, a guy. . . . After that accident, on our honeymoon, I began playing the clown for you. All the time. Now I'm not clownish any more. People say I'm too serious. . . . I spoke to my father and they said come and visit and I told them I wanted to bring a friend and my father said, 'Not in my house. You'll sleep in separate bedrooms.' " She laughs, this is hilarious to her. "I do have someone who's important to me now, not Mitchell. He's not important. He's just a good driver. We were stuck in all that mud, you know. A lot of people who heard what you did—it made them re-evaluate their own lives. It made them stop and think."

We went in to eat. Mitchell still had my shirt on. The food didn't go down well. I had a pain in my stomach and a headache.

"I'll probably have to have an operation on my hand," I tell her.

No reaction.

"Chew more slowly. Do you like it?"

"It's really great," said Mitchell from the couch.

Paula goes out to the kitchen for more food. I get up and go to Mitchell.

"Look, this is where I lived for three years. Mostly good years too. This is a nightmare seeing you here in my shirt and on my sofa and with my children. In the hospital I learned something about how I control my anger, how bad it is to control emotion like that. I'm controlling it right now just talking to you like this. I'm telling you this because I'm angry at you and I might do something to you if you keep sitting here in my shirt."

Mitchell stops eating. He gets up and walks out.

Paula walks back in. She stops in the next room and talks to Mitchell. He leaves the apartment. She comes into the living room.

"You hurt his feelings. He felt your bad vibrations."

"I was being honest with him."

"What would violence accomplish?"

"I just told him how I felt."

"Do you want to leave?"

"It's this environment that does it. It's my apartment. I'm still paying the rent. I'm only allowing you to live here."

"Soon you'll have your own environment and I'll have mine. It'll be easier."

"I don't think you understand what I've been through. If you had any feeling for other people you

wouldn't have pulled this, having him here in my
shirt the first time I come up."

She went to wake up Suzie. That way we wouldn't
have to talk. She tried feeding her but she wouldn't
eat. She went in to do the dishes. Tommy was ready
for his bath. I had given him a bath in that repainted
bathroom a hundred times, two hundred times
maybe. I just couldn't stand being there any more. I
left. Good-bye.

Saul and Annie were amazed. Stunned. A kid?
Wearing your shirt? How could she? She knew you
were coming. She talks about love and good vibrations and all that Woodstock jazz and look what she
did to you, Annie said. Are you okay? Are you feeling all right? Saul volunteered to go over and kill the
kid.

When I told Nathanson the next day, he asked if
she were seeing a therapist. She's patronizing to you.
She treats you like a helpless kid, he said. It's material for a novel. Didn't you get angry? he asks. How
could you stay for dinner? he asks. I ask him: how
can I go up there and see my kids and face that
madness? His eyes. Can't you answer that yourself?
Thirty bucks please.

Thursday morning. I go to the hospital to see another hand doctor for another evaluation. Well, two
tendons. Extensor longus. Abductor. We could fix it.

How did you do it? Oh. I'm sorry. Anytime after Labor Day. You'd wear a cast for about three weeks, maybe four weeks. A cast? Now? Oh no. I drive away with the New York *Times* real estate section. I call two brokers. I check the listings in the *Village Voice*. I see an apartment on West 72nd Street. It makes me nauseous to think of living there. I look at one on West 82nd Street. Same reaction. Fear and nausea. It doesn't seem possible to picture myself living in these places. Not possible at all. How can I? All day I check with agents up and down the West Side. I look at more apartments the next day, Friday morning. Too small. Too noisy. A lousy street. Too expensive.

After leaving Nathanson's on Friday I meet Vicki as prearranged with Paula. Why am I meeting you, she asks. She is a large girl, dark-haired, with a sweet face. About those apartments? I ask. Oh yes. Well, my boyfriend sold his loft, our loft. The people moving into the loft are about to have a baby so we have to get out soon. The landlord in your building wants to rent it to someone already. So you'll have to speak to him, okay? (I don't understand any of this. How did this suddenly get to be *my* problem?)

Now then, you take the Charles Street apartment, Jesse. I'll run through it again. My friend Barbara is living there now. She's a painter. It's my apartment. I sublet it to her. She's going to Europe in the next week or two and as soon as she leaves you get

the apartment. She'll live somewhere else when she
gets back. Do you want to go see the apartment
now? She calls her friend. No answer. Try her Saturday, says Vicki. She knows all about it. Let's have
a drink.

We sit down at an outdoor table at the Riviera.
Look, I explain, to me this was just an impulse on
Paula's part. I don't think it's all going to work out
the way you want. There are too many people involved. Paula's not all that— Oh yes, says Vicki,
seeing me grope for words. I can see that about
Paula. I mean, I was supposed to meet her today
and take her to the East Village to find her an apartment. I know the streets and everything over there.
I waited two hours until finally I called up and some
guy named Mitchell said she drove to Pennsylvania
because her mother was upset and having a nervous
breakdown or something. If I hadn't called her, I'd
still be waiting. And I wouldn't have known I was
supposed to meet you over there. I see, I tell her.
Paula told me you would be wearing a yellow flower.
Vicki looks at me like she knows this is all ridiculous,
this apartment stuff, for the first time. That she
made a mistake. "Well," she says, "Paula never told
me about the yellow flower."

She calls Barbara again. Still not home. I don't
know what else to do, she says. I can't take an apartment sight unseen, I say. They're two small rooms,

she says. They can fit easily into your living room.
It's on the sixth floor.

Good-bye, Vicki. I'll see Barbara on Saturday.

Friday. I cancel dinner with my parents for tonight.

Apartments. Indecisive. The Sunday *Times* real
estate section. Buzzing around in Saul's borrowed car.
A man in his building, Mr. Goshorn, works for the
Times. A typographer. Grave moral responsibility,
he tells me. He won't discuss it with me on the
phone. Meets me at the door. Talk about getting
the Sunday real estate section on Friday. When you
go down there, he tells me, looking down the hall
this way and that to make sure no one's listening,
you ask for Mr. C. Fourth floor. I've spoken to him.
He'll give you a copy. You must understand my
position, he says. You're getting the jump on people.
Is that fair? Is that moral? He shakes his head:
I don't know if I should be doing this. I don't even
know you.

I go to the *Times* and get the copy. And after all
that, it's just a bunch of broker listings. Having the
paper that Friday afternoon, two days ahead of time,
does me no good whatever. Every listing that weekend is a broker ad.

That night I go to a picnic in the park with

Saul and Ann, their kids, and some friends of theirs
from NYU—drama teacher, political science teacher
and wife, clergyman and wife. Chicken, cheese and
wine. I drink a lot.

After, Saul leaves for a meeting. Ann and I stay
up till midnight talking. She tells me that her college
roommate was flipping out when they lived together
and that she, Ann, didn't know it till years later,
and felt awful when she finally realized it.

Saturday morning. I see Mr. Goldstein's brownstone on West 74th Street. Horrible. Two hundred
twenty dollars a month. Third floor. Can't see myself in a life there.

I head down to Nathanson's in Saul's borrowed
red car. I have an orange juice at the Colony.
Nathanson says the reason I'm scared of taking an
apartment is my fear of being alone, of living alone,
that I'm still holding on to my marriage. No apartment is an irrevocable move, he says, and you can't
procrastinate forever. I know all this. I can hardly
talk. My throat feels stuck. As stuck as my insides.
He says Saul and Annie sound like warm parents. He
asks me if I am especially scared about being out
of the hospital. On the way out I check his wall
diplomas. I discover something strange: he didn't
graduate from medical school until 1963. That would
make him younger than me. I'm beginning not to
like his ways, his cold stares and his fat puffy face.

Saturday afternoon.

Barbara. Six flights up over Charles Street and Sheridan Square. It's the smallest apartment in the world. I can hardly believe it. Barbara is beautiful though. Soft and dark. Maybe twenty-four or so. On the small side. A beautiful quiet voice. The two rooms overflow with paints and canvas. A lot of portraits. Views of traffic outside. Rumbling train noises down there. She's a pretty good painter.

"I like it here. It's like a nest. I don't really want to leave." She speaks softly, barely above a whisper. In that little apartment anything louder is a shout. "What did Vicki tell you?"

The apartment swapping story again.

"You write novels, Vicki told me. What are they about?"

"One of them is about trying to find an apartment."

She laughs. And this time I say nothing about life imitating art or cosmic grinning cruelties.

She gives me tea and a cigarette. I like her portrait of Vicki. I like most of her stuff. "When I came back from Paris the brownstone I'd been living in on the West Side jumped from $145 a month to $180 a month in just one year."

My bandaged wrist protrudes from the wrist of my jacket, the cuff. Does she see it? What does she think of it? I picture myself in bed with her. What's

her last name? One day, when I can start again
with women, I'll call her. "You can stay here while
I'm in England if you want," she offers.

Back at Saul's in the late afternoon. We have coffee
and then head over to my old apartment to pick
up my typewriter and a sweater. I called first.
Mitchell there. I am full of pains in the stomach
and pulling at my beard. I hate going to that building, seeing old neighbors who know what I did and
the doormen. Saul is making jokes, but he sees my
fear. "This guy Mitchell knows you're coming,
right?" I nod.

The doorman has magazines and mail. "Does
someone have a key?" he asks. "Been a lot of people
there the last few days." Saul and I exchange looks.

Mitchell opens the door. I was right: he doesn't
shave yet. We go in, Saul wary, like he'd like to
swing at him, pacifist that he is. The place is an
unbelievable mess. Ashes on the floor. Smelling pissy
and brown ricey. Clothes strewn on all the chairs.
Cups and glasses and crusted dishes laying around
on chairs and on the floor. "Jesus," Saul mutters
under his breath, glancing around, shaking his head.
Under the dining-room table I see the shirt he was
wearing the other day. I get a bathing suit in the
bedroom. Then the typewriter. Then a sweater.

The bell rings. Mitchell lets in a skinny guy. He

smells vile. We shake hands. "Hey man, can I play some beautiful music on that piano?" he asks. I nod. I collect some papers. Saul looks pained. He's had dinner here with us, brought his kids to play many times, come to parties, watched movies. He knows what the place looked like. I go into the living room. The jacket the piano player is wearing lies on the sofa. Mitchell is sitting on the sofa reading a book. About twenty books and some beer cans are on the floor at his feet. The jacket's label—*mine*. Hey, were you wearing that jacket? Empty the pockets, I order him. Empty them! Saul advances into the living room. The piano player empties the pockets. He looks hurt. "I apologize," he says. "I was hung up." "I mean for Chrissake," I try to tell him. "This is really—I'm still a person! I'm still alive! I still exist!" I say it even if I don't feel it. How do I stand it?

We take some jackets and clothes at Saul's suggestion and we leave. Downstàirs in the car he expresses his shock. He can hardly find the words. "It's really incredible. It's really incredible. If you don't feel absolutely lousy there'd be something wrong with you. Are you okay?"

All this writing is so calm. So flat. Just declarative sentences. It's all so literal. Facts. Where is the heat? Shouldn't it sound enraged?

Nathanson: I tell him I am thinking a lot about
suicide again. It is all more than I can handle. I
will never get an apartment and live by myself. I
feel a burden to Saul and Ann. I discuss the idea of
going back into the hospital again. He doesn't think
it'll do much good. I am not afraid of death. I am
afraid of life. I confirm that to him. Why are you
so afraid of supermarkets and buying food and cooking? he asks. He suggests I think it's effeminate.
That my mother did it for me, that she did everything for me. I find that I am unable to express
myself talking to him. I can sit perfectly quiet for
half the time. Sighing. Staring. Looking for words.
Starting sentences, thoughts, and not knowing what
I want to say, how to finish. Saul asked if I really
thought writing books was harder than cooking. If
that was true, he said, then I'm really crazy.

We go out on a Sunday outing, Tommy and Suzie
and Ann and Saul and their three kids. To a friend's
at the beach. Tommy seems hungry all the time.
When he sees people eating tomatoes he says they'll
make your brains mushy. An adult contradicts him.
So does Carol, one of Saul and Ann's kids. "They
do *not*." They get into a discussion of brains and
tomatoes. "Milk doesn't make you white," he is ad-

vised. Later in the day he has a Coke and he drinks it as though he is doing something very wrong and really enjoying it. I play football with them on the beach. Lou's passes are hard. I felt close to death, head tingling, skin prickly, feverish, body aching, nose running. I caught head to the right, letting the ball hit my right arm. Only once did I take a pass to the left and I saw stars when the ball hit my hand, like an explosion in my wrist. Eight hours at the beach. We drive back through the smog. Saul drops me off. I take the kids up. "I'll be all right," I assure him.

Upstairs I tell Paula to go easy on this food thing, that it's getting him all fucked up about food. He's all anxious about it. He prefaces every bite with, "That shitty food will make me sick." But he likes cheese and watermelon and ice cream and he eats it anyhow, feeling guilty and wondering what his mother will say.

She demands an immediate accounting of everything he's had to eat. "Did you eat the chicken?" (She provided him with chicken and cous-cous—*organic* chicken.) He nods. "A little."

"Paula, cut it out. This isn't necessary. Don't get him so upset about a simple thing like eating."

"What poison did you feed him today? I want to know. Tell me!"

He starts to cry. He's been fine all day. He was a little worried about eating with me. We flew a kite

on the beach, dug holes. He kicked a ball. I lifted
him over waves and he screamed and shrieked. Now,
after stories in the car on the way back and kisses
and hugs, he's crying. Paula screams on, the fiend in
her really coming out.

"I have my beliefs about food. He'll eat the right
food and not your poisons. He'll have a bellyache
every time he goes out with you, *every time!*"

"Only if you tell him that. If you had his interests
at heart you wouldn't say a thing like that in front
of him."

Her eyes are grim in their hatred of me. "You'll
get a bellyache when you see your father, if that's
what you want," she tells him.

"Stop it! You're crazy," I yell at her.

My son is now screaming-crying.

I gather him up. "Don't go," he cries. "I don't
want you to go."

"Will you get out of here already," Paula screams.
"Look at how upset you made him. Go. You'll get
used to this. It's not the first time, it won't be the
last."

I hug him and leave. In the hall I cross paths
with the black girl in miniskirt who I've never seen
before. A new occupant of my once-quarters. And
my baby girl is out in the hall, crying. She looks mad,
vacant, as mad and vacant as her mother. I can't do
anything but leave. Tommy is roaring-screaming in
the back bedroom. If I had a machine gun I would

take both kids out in the hall and then shoot Paula
and throw her and the black girl out the window.
This is so awful, so horrible. How do I stand this?
How will my son stand living with this lunatic?
She'll drive him crazy. It's so unfair. Happiness is
gone. We are all doomed.

At the beach, earlier, I remembered so many
beach days with Paula. I remembered making it with
her in the shower in my parents' house the summer
before in Long Beach. Working at the cabana club
there when I was in college. Playing tennis that
summer. All I do is remember. Remember. Remember. Another life I remember. A former life.
Was it that I didn't know what I was doing then
—or now? The visits to Long Beach to my parents
in the Volkswagen when we were married. Paula
and the dog and Tom. Swimming with the dog, the
way she took the breakers. My mother's cream cheese
and tuna-fish salad dinners in the summer. My
father in his ill-fitting bermudas, my son getting red.
Oh God. *Oh God.* I am so sad, so very sad. How
do I continue going through the motions of being
alive? Do I keep thinking of guns for nothing?
Would that be the quickest way? Where do you do
it? In the mouth? The temple? The ear? Who would
clean up the mess? Can I fit a hose on the tail pipe
of a car? Which car would have the right kind of

side-vent window? I would need a quiet, isolated
spot, maybe where I went to camp when I was a
kid. In the fall, at night, it would be deserted there.

Why do I want to go on? Do I have any curiosity
about what else there is? I'm so tired and exhausted.
All the time exhausted. I don't want to illuminate
pages. This confessional is ugly and pathetic.

When would I have the operation? I can't face
that at all. It means being in a sling and a cast
for a month. Impossible. How can I go up to that
apartment again and face all those creeps there?
How can I see Paula again? Everything I do is full
of pain. The emptiness of the present. (Saul is a
beautiful father. His three children. They sing and
talk and eat and they're happy and full of light.)
I am the guy in the baby's room, turning the air
conditioner on and off, smelling up the place with
sweat, afraid, afraid, afraid. I haven't called my
lawyer in a while. I can't chance another complica-
tion. I spoke to a landlord, and said no to three
apartments he showed me. All these words and I
find nothing here. Nothing. Saul and Ann are protecting me from myself. When I'm alone who will
protect me from myself? I'm plucking out the hairs
of my beard one by one, hundreds of little wiry hairs,
thousands of them. My beard is so sparse.

Sometimes all this writing seems too calm. Is it

my ability that is at fault? Maybe I really can't find the words. They don't convey how I feel. Where is the heat? Where is the anger? Where is rage? Where is emotion? Gone. Just declarative sentences. Flat quickies.

August 29.
The theft. Paula laughs about. Man, it's just things. Possessions.
No, it's theft. They're crooks.
She doesn't care.
Nathanson wanted to know why I hadn't moved my things out. He was under the impression I had already done it.
The cops were incredulous. The insurance company, too. Paula is suspected of collusion.
Nathanson: You don't see the danger signals, the flashing red lights. Others do.
Beard plucking and wrist scar visible. Everybody can see it. It's public. It's also self-castrating. Masochistic.
Tommy: it's easier on him. There's someone to take care of him. You, Jesse, you want someone to take care of you: Nathanson.
Nathanson: how about your beard? Why do you wear it? Don't the old Jews pluck at it? Does it cover your adolescent acne scars you keep telling me about? Weak chin? Because your mother dislikes it?

You're afraid of fantasies, not the real thing: Nathanson.

Fears of loneliness and abandonment. You've always had them. Now they've come true.

Don't be afraid of doors. They open both ways— both in and out. They let you come in and they let you go out.

You sit here and stutter and tell me about some guy sleeping with your wife, wearing your shirt; do you rip it off his back, explode, walk out, yell???? But *not* stay for dinner. Where is your anger? Doesn't it sound odd?

You change the subject and overwhelm me with details. You want support, not therapy.

What are your worst fears? You should be able to guess at them by now: Nathanson.

Babies crying in the background. People talking. Movement. It's good. I like it. Better than silence. Saul cooks breakfast. I do nothing to help. I take.

All I want to do is sleep, sleep, sleep. Withdraw. Catatonically. What will ever make me come out of this?

I abdicate the struggle. Let the others win. Will I ever laugh uproariously again? Ever have an orgasm inside a woman again? Ever love? Dance? Ever wake up from this living death?

I am so sick of my sufferings, sick to death, sick to life.

The people around me are too happy. I see them on the streets. They laugh and bite deeply into their peaches.

These past few months haven't been my whole life and yet they feel that way. My exhausted state has gone on so long I don't remember what it was like before. The question I ask myself: have I exhausted myself totally, my resources, my being, my machinery, my vital parts. To exhaust oneself completely is for the fuel tank to run dry. And for there to be no fuel supply to replenish the tank, and no entrance, no opening, no orifice.

I used to think certain things in this world were constant—the sunrise, darkness, a mother's love, a wife.

I still feel I can't take care of myself. Do Saul and Ann know that? Do they indulge me in it?

I'm getting more and more involved in oral gratification. It's a limited sense but it's something and it can seem important when nothing else at all seems important or desire-quickening. I like to eat now. Eating is one of my very few pleasurable acts. Very primitive.

On the way to Nathanson's today I am thinking of driving this car all the way to California, of get-

ting my money from the local bank and just taking
off. Getting a new social security card. Never writing them again, never hearing about what happened. I tell him. He stares at me and says nothing. "But I can't help it," I tell him. "That's not
me talking, that's not me thinking. I'm living with a
madman, a depressed madman inside me. I hate
what he does. I hate the way he gives up. I hate
the way he whines and the way he says 'I can't.'
I hear his voice and hate the tone of it. He's an
idiot. But I can't stop him. He won't leave me. He
won't work. He won't look at girls. He won't fight.
He won't leave me alone. I'm sharing my life with
a goddam fucking creep."

"You know you're doing to yourself," he says.
"There's no one else in there with you. It's you."

We stare at each other.

"Do you want to get better?" he asks. "Because,
that's the question."

I am sick of my sufferings, sick to death, sick to
life.

I still feel like I can't take care of myself. In
the morning at Saul and Ann's I make the bed.
That's it. The rest they do, the cooking and shopping. I make a pretense of looking for an apartment.

I've stopped looking for exit signs.

I've stopped looking for entrance signs.

I don't care about anything.

I have no desires.

I am my own assassin.

I am watching a movie of my own life disappearing.

I have no freedom, I know I don't.

I see my son in ten years, annihilated, blaming me with his eyes. Why did you leave me with her?

I will keep on writing this horror story till the last day.

And in the middle of this I am writing a book review. Poor writer, if he only knew.

How did I write all those books and things? Because writing is therapeutic? Because I didn't know what else to do with my time?

Writing is a substitute for living. But what choice has the writer? None. The reader has a choice. He doesn't have to read.

To die is to forget.

I see my son in ten years, fifteen years, blaming me, accusing me. Desertion, he'll say. Coward. Emasculated weakling. Why did you leave me with her?

If he's not crazy by then. I pray for the continuance of his sanity. It's beyond sadness. It's beyond tragedy. It's the annihilation of four lives.

Most people say "maybe" to life. Not absolutely

"yes" to life nor completely "no" to death. Look at all the deathly things life-people do. What I see here is the sort of thing I used to think I could only see under drugs. But look: I can still see into things a little even if I can't express it very well. I might even be willing to endure further agonies, as an experiment. To come over to the other side, to the living side, after all this, would make me some kind of a freak, a living, breathing, Evangelist-meeting-example of faith, of man's superimpenetrability and indomitability. Living could even be kind of fun. What was it like?

I must be special. My agent keeps trying to impress me with the fact that I was alone, unique among all her clients, that I never had a writing block and all the others did, do.

At my parents' house, my father starts in about the money, and the insurance. He pores over my old check stubs. "What's this one for—clothes? Again clothes? How much clothes could the two of you buy in one year? When you got all that money you were like a child. Why didn't you come to me? I would have helped you. . . . And this one? A typewriter? Well, you can show it to them. You'll collect. You've got to have proof, though. Proof! Really, if I didn't see it with my own eyes, I wouldn't have

believed it. You keep lousy records, mister. Really
lousy. How do you expect—?"

When he is silent, watching me pick through cartons of papers, he clicks his teeth and does something new and weird with his gums. A sound I never
heard him make before.

They are two incredible human beings. She just
prattles on about her friend who has a new butcher
and how terrific she claims his meat is. It is all so
devastating. No wonder I wrote funny books once.
No wonder I am what I am.

It's all true. I have inherited their caution. I have
inherited their fears. I have inherited their limits.
I have inherited their madness. I am them. Once
I threw them aside and now I am back to them.

A day of days. Saul helps me move my books and
cabinets and shelves out of the old apartment.
Rather, he does it all. Unscrewing standards, taking
out air conditioners. Packing boxes. I walk around in
circles. Paula screams: Don't touch this, don't take
that. She hides things in the bathtub and in closets.
She carves up my desk chair with a knife, screaming.
I disarm her and raise the knife. Saul grabs my
arm. The Puerto Rican mover tells me he got four
years for taking a shot at his wife. "I only fired
at the ceiling," he says. "Don't kill her. It's not
worth going to jail. Leave her alone." Advice from

a Puerto Rican mover. "Just don't talk to her," he tells me. "Don't listen to her." While Saul carries stuff out with the movers she runs around making Indian whoops, or sing-songing, "Oh he can't get it up, he can't get it up." She insists on keeping all the copper and rings from trips to Turkey and India. "You can't have any of your stuff unless I keep this." Maybe I should just kill her and pay the penalty. I can always escape. What else would do besides her death?

Lawyer Weiss: "You're getting off cheap if she's taken a forty-dollar-a-month apartment like she says."

And after seeing him I take a taxi back home and go back to sleep, from ten thirty to one, when Casey calls.

"How are the kids?" he asks. "Are they in good shape? . . . Jesse? Were you sleeping? . . . You sound low."

The weather is changing. Getting colder.

September 12. Erev Rosh Hashonoh. I took an apartment and then turned it down, depressed by the street, 79th between nowhere and a funeral parlor, a slum in West San Juan. I already paid the broker. Somehow I'll get the money back.

That afternoon. Nathanson.

"You're not facing your fears. You're still not getting an apartment and striking off on your own. When will you do it? What are you so afraid of?"

But I must get back to work. Yesterday I retyped ten pages on my manuscript. A feat. It was tiring, but I did it. Ten pages retyped used to be a couple hours' easy work, but not now. It could be that my work will save me, as it has in the past.

I wonder if by the end of this notebook I'll have slept with a woman.

Barbara and I had dinner in the village, an Italian place. We talked and talked and talked. When she told me she went to Barnard I made a face. "Is that where Paula went?" she asked. Yes.

She told me how much she liked reading Virginia Woolf. She liked her time sense, her sensitivity, what she called the quiet on her pages.

"Why did Virginia Woolf kill herself?" she asked.

I confessed I didn't know.

"She walked into the ocean," Barbara said.

Barbara had the fettucini and I had the cannelloni. She went to Music and Art High School. She grew up in Washington Heights, of all places. She was twenty-seven, more than I had thought. Did I

say she was beautiful? She is. I didn't tell her she
was the first girl I had gone out with since Mary in
April. May, June, July, August, and now September.
A long time for sexual desire to be extinct. Diag-
nosis: impotence brought on by disinterest in life.
Disinterest in women is disinterest in life and no
fucking around about it.

After dinner we walked and talked for an hour.
(I brought her wine and flowers when I arrived
earlier. Like a kid come courting.) At her building
she doesn't invite me up. We talk at the stoop. We
make a date for Sunday.

Friday afternoon I get the Sunday *Times* real estate section early. Why do I go through the motions?
I'm going to die anyway. I can't continue living
this way. Nothing there. Only brokers. An ad says
it wants a quiet man for a Village apartment. An
apartment on West 79th Street through a broker.
A depressing street.

Sunday evening. I meet Barbara at Loews Tower
East to see *Medium Cool*. She is wearing a knitted
green dress and a shawl. She looks like a gypsy. Or
Portuguese. A year ago, suddenly. The Chicago on-
slaught. I met the actress at Sam's house recently,
nice Jewish girl from Boston playing a sexy Okie in

Chicago. A good movie, but they didn't have to die at the end. It was foolish.

After the movie we wander down Third Avenue. This is our second date. She turns out to be Jewish! She doesn't look it. Everyone is Jewish. The whole world. Her father changed his name. The second day of Rosh Hashonoh this is. Past the antique shops strolling at nine o'clock. My arm around her black shawl. I come up short. Right ahead, twenty steps up, there's Mrs. Craig, the big black nurse from Winston. With a pack of patients strung out on the sidewalk. I recognize Linda: she still walks stiffly, hands at her side, as though she's in a daze.

"What's the matter?" Barbara asks.

I explain who they are, and how I felt when she led me around the city.

"I never heard of the hospital. Where is it?" she askes. What else is there to ask? Do you still feel you're crazy? Or something like that?

We have hamburgers and beer at an outdoor cafe, corner of 55th and Third. She's in therapy now too, with a woman she likes a lot. It hardly costs anything because she got into it through some community service deal. A two-month process till they approved her. We get into Paula and the kids, the transformation of her, her wanting to do the East Village scene, the kids on macrobiotics, how she's gotten rid of their bed and crib and intends for them to sleep on the floor down there.

She wants to take a subway back but I am a
fiend for taxis. I must have spent a hundred dollars
in two or three weeks just taking taxis everywhere.
I never take the train. Occasionally the bus. She
smokes cigarettes like crazy. I don't touch her in the
taxi. She's not easy to figure out. I don't know where
to start. Will she invite me in this time? At her
corner we get out. Key in lobby door. Up we go.
She's got a new lock upstairs she has trouble with.
She puts on the record player. Want some of that
wine you brought?

We look at her roofscapes and self-portraits. Each
self-portrait is different from the next. Each looks
like a different girl. We talk and smoke and talk
and smoke, and I say something about her eyes and
then I'm kissing her, and her mouth is soft, and
I'm thinking, how strange to clasp your mouth to
another's, to lick tongues and swap saliva as though
I'd forgotten, it has been so long. At first there's no
response from down below, and then it starts
swelling and I'm happy it's alive, that I'm not
destroyed there. Thinking how important Barbara is,
this girl, the first in so long, and I go on necking,
savoring her little kisses, hearing her breathing and
I go into her legs, smooth and firm, not stubbly and
tubby and big like Paula's, and my right hand goes
inside her panties and there's no resistance. It is
going to happen. Oh Barbara, and you're so beautiful, so shy and sensitive but look now how passionate

underneath, a lover at that, with an electric pussy that goes like crazy to my out-of-practice groping. She wriggles and bucks frantically. I've found her good places, what she likes. I wish it were me in there. She appears to come. My hand is aching. I take off her clothes, my clothes. And more kissing and fondling her, beholding her beauty and then I pull her up onto me, astraddle, and I've gotten into such a state that I come too fast but at least I know I still work and I go on and on, and she comes again.

She sits on me for another half hour while we talk. She has firm upright breasts that Rodin couldn't have bettered. An immaculate lean brown body, hard brown belly. More cigarettes. I tell her she's the first woman I've been with in three months. She says nothing. An hour later, two o'clock or so, we make love again, this time her on bottom, and longer.

"Something to eat?" she asks after.

She feeds me, takes care of me. Hots up some lentil soup she's made. And a rice-and-eggplant thing. At eight o'clock, she says, she had to take care of her friend's kid. I take my yellow shirt and striped pants that I got out before the thieves broke into the apartment. In the taxi going uptown I am exhausted and inert. I sleep.

Next morning I smile at breakfast.

"Oh yeah?" says Saul.

"Oh *good,*" says Ann.

I head down to the agent and take the apartment on the seventh floor on the building I looked at yesterday, on 86th, between West End and Riverside. But it's been rented, he tells me. So I take the one on the second floor, facing back. With an old people's home next door. But it's a familiar neighborhood. Two hundred twenty-five bucks for two small rooms. We argue about the price, but the old Jew is adamant. You'll need a letter from your accountant, he says, and a letter from your agent, and samples of your work. When it's semiprofessional they check but not too much, he says. I write him a check. It is September 20.

Tuesday evening I go over to agent Elaine's.

She gets high, or, rather, she is already high when I get there.

"Look, what the hell's under that bandage? Take it off already. Are you going to wear it forever?"

I take it off.

"Oh, *that's* not so terrible."

I explain I'm sparing myself the view of slashes and angry gashes. I don't want to be reminded of the mutilation. I don't want everyone to see it.

"But don't you see it only calls everyone's attention to it, a big white thing like that on your wrist. Nobody would notice it without the bandage."

(Next day Nathanson said: *"I* could have told you to take it off, but *you* have to make that decision, not me. You let Elaine make the decision for you.")

Elaine keeps talking: "You've never been tortured. Really, really tortured. You've never been all the way down there. You never had writer's block. All my other writers die a million deaths over their work and you just sit there, year after year, turning the stuff out with never a letup. You were my freak writer. So now you're like the rest of them: you're suffering."

She sipped her drink.

Elaine: "It's not Paula. It's *you.* You're like a baby! I mean, I'm forty. You're not forty. Be thankful for that. My husband has been through this business twice and he survived. His first wife threw him out and then he threw the second one out. . . . His fourth wife is probably about thirteen at the present moment."

The movers brought the stuff in on Friday. All the fifty boxes, piling up and piling up, and I'm dying in this little place. Some pictures seem to be missing. A montage of photographs—framed—from Israel. And an Arab rug. As soon as the movers leave, I leave.

Saturday Saul helps me put up bookshelves. Rather, *he* puts them up. We hem and haw and go over the disposition of the furniture, planning and considering and reconsidering. While he puts the shelf brackets and standards into the wall, I pull on my beard and run back and forth to the hardware store buying anchors and plugs and such.

Back at his place, in the early evening, and Annie's pissed because it's almost seven o'clock, and the baby-sitter, and the kids haven't had baths and he's looking guilty and I feel shitty, but I'm grabbing for support *everywhere* and I can't feel too embarrassed. I dash off to Barbara's, in a taxi, and she's got a fried chicken going there. She's quiet as a mouse sometimes, compliant and soft and so gentle. She's a very good artist, but I'm beginning to see the fucked-up side of her more and more.

After dinner, and a little television, I say something definitive, like "Let's go to bed." So we skip all necking preliminaries and she unrolls her super-big double-bed sofa thing. It is the first time I stay overnight. Only a fair performance. But how great it is to fall asleep in bed with a girl. How wonderful. I'd forgotten. She sleeps on her back. I look at her and look at her. I can't help it. Occasionally she opens an eye and catches me staring. Either she pretends not to notice or assumes I'm harmless. I fall asleep somewhere between four and five.

Then it is nine. Incredibly bright. No window shades. I see a flag outside the window, below, on a pole, a little square on the corner of Charles Street

and Seventh Avenue South. I pull the sheet over my
head. I feel like I haven't slept in a year. Another
fucking day. Even waking up next to Barbara doesn't
dispel the awful morning depression. Another fucking goddam day that I am alive in. I am half awake
for the next few hours, lying next to her, peeking at
her occasionally, sleeping a little, mostly lying there
next to her like a puppy who needs company.

We get up finally at a quarter of two.

My heart is pounding. I tell her I have to go up
to my place to unpack boxes of books and papers.
With a fear that is like death awaits. Why doesn't
Barbara see that I am crazy?

A week later, in my new apartment, I walk
around in circles, trying to decide where things
should go. I walk for an hour. I sweat. I pull at my
beard. It involves making decisions. Boxes are piled
up five high. Mostly books and papers.

I go to the book boxes. Saul has already put up
the standards and shelves for me. I plug the radio
in and turn it on, a constant jabber. I will move in
when they put the phone in next week, when I have
the boxes unpacked. I have to start on this mess.
I have to. Where do you start? Any box. I spill
three or four boxes of books onto the floor. Thomas
Mann. Ernest Hemingway. Joseph Heller. Konrad
Lorenz. John Steinbeck. Kurt Vonnegut. The Bible.

French dictionary. Travel magazine from Africa. Or-
well, Freud, Wolfe, Singer, Elman, O. Henry, John
Horne, Burns, me, Fred J. Cook, Wilhelm Reich,
Ralph Waldo Emerson, Richard Wright, Katherine
Anne Porter, Joseph Conrad, Yael Dayan, Mark
Twain, Meyer Levin, Bruce Jay Friedman, T. E.
Lawrence, Nathanael West, Kathrin Perutz, Dan
Wakefield, Donald Honig, Lewis Mumford. Eight or
nine hundred others waiting to be put up the wall.
I'm staggering after three hours. Who goes where?
Why in this room and not there? Who gets thrown
out? I'm not good at throwing out books. Norman
Mailer, Lenny Bruce, Hermann Hesse.

The next day I tell Nathanson about the boxes.
I don't want to do it, I want to kill mys——

By Tuesday I've put the books up and I start on
the papers and manuscripts and correspondence, the
packages of photos. All those words, articles, reviews, short stories, outlines, a letter from my brother
from 1959, a letter from Burt from 1958, pictures
from my honeymoon, a wedding album, manuscripts.
So many words. Stacks of stuff published in magazines. *The Nation, Ford Times, Village Voice, Pag-
eant, Saturday Review, Ramparts, Literary Review,
Male, Men, True Adventure, Contact.* It's the paper
stuff that's unbelievable. I can't stand it. The drafts
and carbons, first copies and second copies. Early
stories, shredding tissue paper. College notebooks.
Psychology. English 8. Cookbooks. Running dirty

fingers through my hair. Pacing, chain-smoking, eating Oreos. Where do I put the clipping books? What about the first draft of my second novel? What about the galley packages? Baby pictures of Tommy.

I complain to Nathanson again about my whole life swarming before me on that dirty floor. I can't throw it out. I can't decide what to do with it. You should see the mess, I tell him. This is torture. It smells, the old pages smell.

"It's pretty self-destructive," he says. "Why don't you just put it on the shelves in the boxes. In the closets. Why examine it?"

I don't know. I have to.

Leaving Barbara's bed in the morning, at seven, I head uptown to get the car. She asks me to please not be cruel about what I have to do.

A Susan Leventhal drives the cab.

I prowl the streets. I don't find it on Broadway, or on the side streets. I try 106th Street and 107th Street on Riverside Drive. And finally spot it, at 109th and Riverside Drive. I try two garages with it and then the third accepts me, it, and my scheme. I take the plates off.

Before heading down to the Motor Vehicle Bureau I call Paula to tell her what I've done. I am prepared.

"You sneak. You bastard. You thief. I'm going

to fuck up your life so bad you won't believe it. I'm going to get twelve thousand dollars a year out of you." When she calms down she says, "Why don't you find a chick and quit hassling me?" I have, I tell her. "Did you sleep with someone last night?" she asks. Then she gets back to the car. I explain I did it because I am inundated with her parking tickets. Her disregard for meters, for alternate-side-of-the-street parking rules. The car is still registered in my name, I say in my little speech, and I've got $115 worth of your parking ticket summons slips on my desk and so you'd better register the car in your name and you take the consequences. "But I don't have any money for the insurance," she screams. "What happened to the five hundred dollars I gave you last week?" I ask. "I loaned four hundred dollars of it to that black chick who was staying here. She needed it." Incredible. She is crying. I tell her I will pay the first quarter of her insurance. I tell her where to find the car, how to get her FS-1 insurance papers.

Then I go down to the Motor Vehicle Bureau, in a taxi. Then I head up to talk to the detective at the 24th Precinct about the robbery, whether they can do anything about the fact the crook sent Paula a note of regret and apology—from the Brooklyn House of Detention.

He calls the Brooklyn House of Detention, the Brooklyn Criminal Court, all kinds of places. "The

DA could stick it into this guy good and twist it off, if you know what I mean. A guy who writes letters to the people he robs? He's some kind of intellectual. A maniac. This flowery stuff. Any crook when he gets to jail he starts reading books and all of a sudden he becomes an intellectual. Know what I mean? Go see the Brooklyn DA tomorrow, okay pal?"

That ends that.

On the phone, in the evening, Barbara says she is going to Fire Island for the weekend. She has to get out of her apartment for the month because Vicki and her boyfriend are moving in. She says she misses me. She says she'll move in with me when she comes back in a few days.

Next day I head down to see the insurance adjustor at Broadway and Wall Street. I file a fifteen-hundred-dollar claim for the theft. It all sounds very fishy to him. Mr. Bothar. A crew cut and a Marine Corps diploma on the wall. He writes down the story of the theft. Then dictates a statement into a machine, right in front of me. I head back uptown, for some reason on the train, and change my address at the post office. Then to the apartment for more unpacking of trunks and shit. I buy some towels and sheets and silverware and dishes.

I walk around in circles trying to figure out where to put things. Can I really live here? Where should the pictures go? There don't seem to be natural

spaces, natural places for things. Too many decisions.
I don't hang any pictures. How do you live alone?
How do millions of people live alone? It's so un-
natural. It's so scary. I need an electric clock. The
radio floats off the frequency band. I need a new
radio. I need a television set. The rug is filthy. It has
candle-wax drippings all over it. I hang the shower
curtains. They're too short. I empty the last trunk
and throw the trunk out. It is Paula's camp trunk,
with her name-label sticker on the inside.

The kitchen sink has a leak under it. A very dusty
place. I need a strainer, glasses, a coffee maker,
silver foil, plastic storage containers. I need a frying
pan. The window shades haven't come. The windows are ugly-sooty-dirty bare. How would I get
curtains? Where do you measure them from? Paula
always took care of that.

The bathroom sink is cracked. And the lamps
aren't bright enough. The place is too dark. It faces
the back of another building. I need a hanging
lamp. Where do you get them? How do you put
them up? I don't regret throwing out all the fitted
sheets I slept on with Paula. Should I have kept the
tablecloths? No, I'm glad I threw them out, too. I
need a wastepaper basket. I pile stuff into closets.
The foot locker and two filing cabinets stand where
the bed will go. But where will I stuff them when
the bed comes? The radio stays on the whole time

I'm here. I can't bear the quiet. I need some plants,
too. But what kind?
   Back to Saul and Ann's.
   All they have to do is take one look at me.
   Are you okay? they ask.
   Yeah. Ahhhh.

IV

from notebook three a
(*the green one*)

October 4.

Somehow I have lived here, occupied these two shitty prison-rooms, for two whole days. I take taxis to anywhere from here. The money I've spent on taxis. Barbara calls it my perversion.

The new apartment has put me into a new crisis. I am calling up sporting goods stores, checking the yellow pages, ringing up gun stores. I have all the details on how you buy a rifle and get a license. I check a brand name in a book and call up Abercrombie. The gun that Hemingway killed himself with costs six thousand dollars.

And my mother keeps calling up every day to see if I feel better, as though I've had a cold. I know

why they call up. To see if anyone answers, if I'm
still alive.

Nathanson doesn't think I'm in a crisis. He doesn't
think I'll kill myself. He doesn't seem to understand
why I might. I keep telling him I don't care enough
about life, that I'm so tired, too beat to make the
big effort, that if there was a pill I could take,
something quick and painless, I'd do it. But that the
idea of a bridge scares me.

My bills. From Paula's summer rental. Gas and
electricity: $116. An $800 hospital bill, $115 in park-
ing summonses. An old $224 Master Charge bill with
a threatening letter, $500 more wanted by the lawyer
for his retainer. I must change my will officially.
All this confusion I can hardly relate to Nathanson.
He says I want someone to make my decisions for
me. "There are two sides to you: one wants to go on
and the other wants to quit."

He wants to hear more of my ancient history. He
says I am omitting my past entirely while dwelling
on the present. Back there I see only mud, darkness,
and shit.

At a party Sunday at Phil's. His paintings are
displayed everywhere. I think he needs some sales.
I'm one of the first to arrive and last to leave.

I answer a lot of questions about the movie. I am
acutely uncomfortable. I haven't been in a room
with this many people in a long time. I pretend.
I talk modestly to painters, pretty wives, and elderly
teachers.

Joan arrives. We slept together ten years ago, just
before I met Paula. She has worked for the Welfare
Department most of these years. Sam and she have
been buddies. Her parents were alcoholics. She came
to the party with a tall guy with whom she goes to
the races. Over the years I've seen her maybe five
or six times, usually at a party at Sam's house.

She tells me how she's become a gambler. Apparently her boyfriend's interest. The guy says it's
a science with a 40 per cent return.

"Listen," I say, "remember that day you and Phyllis came over? In February? The two of you just
popped in late one afternoon."

From her sudden change of expression I can tell
she is ready to drop the banter about gambling and
talk about things.

Joan: "I knew something was very wrong that
day. Phyllis had no idea what was going on between
you, or else she wouldn't have just popped in like
that. She knew she was a heroine for Paula, her
California trip, the freedom. But that's Phyllis, she's
a gypsy. When you and I were in the living room
they were in the kitchen talking. Phyllis told her
that she didn't know about her life really, about

the incredible loneliness, the wandering. She tried
to tell her she envied her, envied Paula, I mean.
She said it's different for her. You know, you've got
a husband and kids. I mean, really, Jesse, she didn't
encourage her to do anything. You don't think that,
do you? I mean maybe I can understand what's happened to Paula. She got married right out of college.
She maybe never got all that kid stuff out of her
system. She's doing it now."

But also she's mad, I try to tell her.

"She is? Well if she is, try to take the kids away.
Are they all right?"

The eternal question. She sees my guilt. I look
down.

"What kind of shape are you in, Jesse?"

I tell her how at the moment I am my own worst
enemy, how I don't trust Jesse Jacobi.

Joan is sympathetic and warm. She tells me about
her mother who was an alcoholic and her brother
who was in an institution. "We abducted him from
the place and they never came after us." All the
time I was growing up, she says, I was in pain. I
suffered agonies. I wrote journals. It took a lot of
years at college and living alone after before I could
get a grip on life.

She looks great, much better, much surer and
more solid and less nervous than she used to. But
me, I've had my heyday. My beard is deplucked,

dandruff everywhere, clothes gone, apartment tiny,
soul shot. But Joan's okay. Homely girls keep si-
dling up to ask about my books. Joan squeezes my
arm. "Let's see each other, okay? I've got to go.
I've kept him waiting too long. Take care of yourself, Jesse."

Another friend, a face, a girl I knew who grew
up to be a woman, while I stayed a kid and always
will be. For however long always is. Maybe just a
few more days.

Like a fool I get high on the wine and sleepy, so
sleepy, sleepy, sleepy.

They're all over the park. A hundred or a hundred
and fifty in the crew. Ten or twelve trucks and vans.
Gigantic lights. Amazing. It's my life they're doing.
My story. Mine. I set it all in motion. I sit and
talk with the lead actor right under the very tree
where Tommy always looks for that piece of kite.

A publicity man asks me if I can explain what
the story is about. This is incredible. It happened
to me here. Or rather I dreamed most of it up here,
walking the dog through here. Assistant directors
call the actors and actresses by their character
names—*my* names. Unreal isn't the word. It is out
of my life of three years ago, when I was writing it.
The hero has a wife, an apartment up the street.

God! A sound man tells me to get the fuck off the cables and stand in back of him.

Last night I went to sleep at eight thirty. There wasn't anything I wanted to do. Nothing at all. Just expire. Dissolve.

I need a TV, a record player, a broiler pan, a strainer. Things like that.

Morty called about one of my dogs.

Ken called about the other dog.

The window shades arrived!

While putting them up I snap the spring on one of them. When I try to rewind it, holding the spring with my finger, it cuts me. I bleed onto the shade, all smudged red over the shiny crisp, new white shade. It's the first blood I've seen coming out of me since that night in July.

Everyone thinks I'm getting better. Little do they know. The hose attached to the tail pipe in my current favorite. Mercury looks better than Chevrolet for that, I've noticed.

In the evening, at six o'clock, after the shrink session, I taxi home. It's dark. I wait for Barbara's call. I listen to the news over and over a dozen times. Finally, at eight, she calls. Still in Bay Shore, out on the Island. She missed the train. She'll catch

the next one, bringing her into the city at ten. She'll
stay with her friend Judy that night. "It's as good
as Europe," she says. "Better maybe. It's so quiet.
I'm getting lots of painting done. I'm going back
there for a couple of weeks." My heart sinks.

Then I make my tuna-fish sandwich for dinner.
Mayonnaise here. A bowl there. I stuff it down. I
check my bills again: the hospital, parking tickets,
Con Edison, the phone company, lawyer. I write to
change magazine subscriptions, as though con-
templating a future.

I look at my manuscript. I should finish it. I've
retyped twenty or thirty pages in the last few days,
but there's a big section of fifty pages clogging the
thing up. It's sloppy. But I can't seem to avoid doing
something about it. Long-winded. The dialogue in
there lacks grace. Maybe I ought to leave it a while
longer. If I can't make decisions about it, I can't.
If only the pages were in better shape. But then I
finished this first draft back in the early spring when
things were going haywire. I think maybe I wanted
to finish it before the storm burst. Sometimes it seems
a little dated. It must end in tragedy. The tragic
ending must be the last one, not the happy one.
It's those fifty pages I worry about all the time.
I've reread them and reread them and I don't know
how to cut them down any more. I suppose I could
if I understood more of what the book was about
now, but that would require going back and reading

the whole thing from the start and first of all I
can't concentrate and retain things these days and
second of all the subject, and the memories of what
the real events were that it is based on, as well as
what was happening while I was writing it, would
make me sick.

My lawyer calls. He says he told her lawyer that
I'll only pay child support and not alimony. They'll
have to talk it over, he says. Nor has she told her
lawyer her new address in the East Village. Her
lawyer wants to have a long talk with her, says my
lawyer.

I usually wait for a phone call to wake me up
here. It always comes. My parents. Agent. Lawyer.
Her parents. The super to tell me when the window
shades will arrive. The insurance adjustor about the
theft. This morning her parents, at eleven o'clock.
I had been up since probably eight thirty, lying
there under the blankets in a half-awake sweat.
"Well, did you speak to the lawyer? . . . Yes? What
do you think? What did he think?" I am inconclusive. They, though, are overbearing. "Ours suggested
to us we do it—but we need your help. Since you
have no custody agreement yet, you just take the
children to our house and we hold them. She has

to get a habeas corpus to get the kids back but we'll hold them and ask the court to let us keep them by saying she's incompetent. You'll transfer the custody to us, get it?" Her father, shifty, goes on. "Then she'll have to prove herself and they'll take one look at her and force her to undergo psychiatric treatment." They hear my hesitation. I see a monster of an ugly business in this.

"Let me speak to that lawyer again," I say. "Paula I wash my hands of," her father says. "Why are you hesitating? Aren't you worried about those kids? Don't you think she's crazy? The girl is insane, isn't she? You want those children to get tuberculosis?" He finally hangs up on my hesitation.

I start calling.

First the ex-judge lawyer-friend of theirs in New York. It wouldn't be kidnaping, he says. Why didn't you tell me this plan of theirs when we first spoke? I ask. It slipped my mind, he says. He's not for rushing it. Then I called Lou, who says, "You'd be acting in the best interests of the children. The question is, Is she a loving mother but sick in her dealings with others? She can go to their house and just take them away. Is her father going to keep a bodyguard there? She says she's fit and we say she's not. It's at the discretion of the judge. And you can forget the separation proceedings if you do this. What a chain reaction it'll set off. Try to get some medical evidence on the kids. Blood tests and the like." I get my lawyer next, Weiss. "Yeah, it could work. You can start the same action in New York when and if you lose in Pennsylvania, if they'll ever hear it in Pennsylvania. She has no money and won't be able to get much of a lawyer, probably a court-appointed one. The thing is there's incompetency and then there's custody." I am not getting this all straight, all these contingencies, I know I am not. Then I call her mother back and she starts asking me about my medical insurance policy and its number. Why? She won't tell me. She says she can't tell me, that I'll have to trust her. What on earth is happening? Has she gone mad too? Her father will call her to tell her where the kids are, she says. The phone number has been disconnected, she says, where Paula is living. Can I do anything about getting the number turned back on, her mother wants to know.

A typically inconclusive therapeutic session—except that . . . if I really don't care about things, then why am I keeping these shrink appointments?

Afterward, I wander around the corner and browse in Brentano's.

What shall I do tonight? Where shall I eat?

I call Henry.

"You bearded baboon," he shouts. "Get over here."

He's off Fifth Avenue at 16th Street. A short walk.

His wife isn't home. She's shopping.

I stare at his thousands and thousands of wall-to-wall hard-cover books, each one with a jacket, an incredibly neat and tidy one-quarter inch of shelf space in front of each. He tells me about his work: a revision of a play, a new children's book, the new novel going around, Civil War stories for a men's magazine. He's been very prolific lately.

"I've never written an autobiographical line in my life," he says. How strange that he thinks that.

He wants to talk about the Mets. I don't care. He tells me about his money problems. Between he and his wife they're making twenty thousand dollars a year. His plans for going to Bermuda. His wife returns. She does publicity at a publisher. We eat Chinese food. She bought a thirty-dollar dress for five bucks—for the trip to Bermuda, two months off. She's easy-going, good-natured, puts up with Henry's money hang-ups. I feel their problems are trifles. They discuss getting out of the city. By turns he wants to and she doesn't, and vice versa. He tells her about a call that day from Hollywood about a book someone's interested in buying. She gets excited. Five-thousand-dollar advance against fifty-thousand-dollar purchase price. They make plans for spending it.

She asks about Paula and the kids. I'm getting

nervous. "The best I can do is not think about," I
tell her.

I taxi home. In the rain.

A long empty afternoon and evening.

I spent an hour mulling over the movie schedules.
I hit on *Dr. Zhivago* and *The Impossible Years*,
after struggling with the possibilities of *Alice's
Restaurant, Blow-Up, Lolita,* and *Butch Cassidy and
the Sundance Kid.* I head for the theater, Loew's
83rd Street.

I buy ice cream and chocolate kisses. My dinner.

The train-ride sequence is utterly beautiful. The
family breaks up. Someone recently told me the book
sold a million copies in hard-cover, some kind of
record. Starvation. The snow. Zhivago has an affair
with Julie Christie while his wife is pregnant. His
wife disappears to Paris. He gets kidnaped by the
Red Army. Never finds his family again. He's a
broken man. I identify with that. During the other
movie my mind starts to wander. This way is nothing. Where can I go? Let go of the children. Head
for Israel under an assumed name. Get a forged
passport in Canada. Take the train to Montreal
and buy a passport there and no one will ever hear
of me again. Leave them a year's worth of money.
Live anonymously on a kibbutz. Or Australia. Find

the proper moment to jump overboard and drown.
Go to Japan and live in a monastery. Become a
monk. Shave my head. What am I waiting for here?
I've already told Nathanson his way is too slow, too
tortuous. Do you know a better way? he asked me.
There must be one. What will my son say years from
now? Will he be driven mad? I cannot go on this
way for ten years. Or even ten months. Or ten days.
I'm trying to find a way out. Close the door and
disappear. Alec Guinness at the end said they all
disappeared. We see Julie Christie on the street. He
jumps off the train and chases her. He has a heart
attack and dies on the street. Lucky him. More
cigarettes. Occasionally I chain-smoke. I see no solution. Take my money and run. Enjoy it till it runs
out and then kill myself when it's time. I can drown
anywhere. My children will always despise me, the
man who left. It would make them suicide-prone.
Something holds me back. What? I wish I could
name it. I can't come up with the proper plan of
escape. Could I close the door and disappear to
someplace warm? How about a forty-dollar-a-month
place in Ibiza, Spain? I don't speak Spanish. A dic-
tatorship. What would I do there? I am slowly dying of a broken heart. No will power. No energy.
The radio is on WQXR, telling me about the can-
dlelight atmosphere of "Ye Waverly Inn." What
about plastic surgery in Switzerland? And then

what? Still circumspect. I'm holding back from anything rash. In tight control.

Someone said it's like you've got to start all over
again. Someone else said, no, you don't have to start
all over again. And every time I look at my wrist
I see the scars, the slashes and gashes, still red and
fierce-looking. I wish they'd whiten. I remember the
stitches, when they took them out. My parents call.
Come up for dinner. No, I can't make it.

I read recently that if man can survive in Manhattan, he can survive anywhere. I wonder if that's
true. All this is about loneliness and despair as a
way of life. I'm jealous of people in cars. I'm jealous
of other people, of their freedom, their contentments.

Had a beer in a new neighborhood bar, "The
Library." Bars depress me.

Tuesday night the date I had with Pam Kelly
was broken. Pam Kelly, ace book editor. She had a
cold. The void for the night. I called Jean and
George, hadn't spoken to them or seen them in at
least a year. Yes, I could come for dinner. Great!
But just as I am leaving the apartment, at seven
o'clock, Paula turns up, with Tommy and Suzie and
some toothless old black man who looks fifty, a five-

day white-stubbled growth, red eyes and red lips. Who the hell *is* he?

"I wanted to borrow the drill. Can I see your place? Oh, this is nice. Look at the way you put up the books. It's so neat."

The black guy puts Suzie down. Paula is wearing a floor-length woolen dress and a fur piece and a knapsack. She looks mad, mad-insane. "I'm going to Pennsylvania tomorrow to see my mother. She's ready to crack up. They may have to institutionalize her. I want to take her to Esalen. It's my father's problem. It's *his* woman. It often happens that a mother cracks up after a daughter goes through some heavy changes. There's a lot of it going around. Can you take the kids on Sunday? I'm going to the Fort Dix demonstration. When the kids stay here, they can sleep on the floor. They're not into beds any more."

I want Saul and Ann to see her, and the black guy, to see if it's only my warped viewpoint that feels she's crazy. I send her over there, and tell her the drill is with them. Then I go to Jean and George's for dinner and block it all out.

Saturday I roam the streets. I head down Broadway and stop in at Casey's loft. He has a small studio in the Seventies. It used to be his friend's, a painter, who is away on a trip. It looks down right

on to the street. Seventy-eighth Street, I think.
Beds on the floor and mats. A hot plate. A desk
and a typewriter stand. Olympic typewriter. He offers me a drink, some coffee. I hem and haw. He's
looking at me like I'm crazy. Finally get to the
Paula business. He's all for compassion. You don't
owe her any reparations. Some of her values aren't
so bad, he says. Let her do her thing. Fuck 'er.
See your kids. You got something to offer them. Don't
fuck around with her parents. Don't. Butchers do
that. Her parents are sixty. They fucked her up and
they could fuck up your kids too. . . . He doesn't
think my shrink is helping me. He's got a good
shrink. Hal Stein. He wants me to say something
definite. We have some bologna and he starts criticiz-
ing my books. "I know there's been some strangeness
between us, what with you reviewing my books and
all, but look, here's what I feel about your work."
And he tells me. "You don't allow your characters
to show their emotions." I choke on a piece of bread.
I try washing it down with wine. "Did I say something wrong?" "No, but that's what the shrink
always tell me about myself. It's funny. . . ." His
own daughter is in good shape. So's his ex-wife. I
was Paula a year ago, he says. I flipped out. I fucked
everyone. Ellen went catatonic. I can help her. You
can help Paula. She can help you. You know what I
mean? You know what I'm saying? You can be a
different person six months from now. How are you

with girls? Does it help? I had Marilyn for the
summer, last summer. A girl was with me. It worked
out. I got six hundred pages written. . . . I start to
go. . . . Stay, don't go. You haven't come to a con-
clusion. Don't do the awful business about dragging
the kids off. Maybe she'll see a shrink. (She won't I
assure him.) Well, then you see a better one who can
help you to get to yourself. Your present one doesn't
sound like much of a person. . . . I listen to everyone. I'll call his shrink. . . . When you walked in
here today you looked like hell, absolute hell. Calm
down. Sure, I think. But do what?

We head out together. He calls his dinner appointment to say he'd be late. We spent five hours
together. He gives me a big bear hug when we part.

Home, I call Paula to see about the kids tomorrow. She tells me a horror story of how her father
beat her and she left their house in Pennsylvania.
Her father schemed out something with a visiting
brother from Akron. The father grabbed her when
the mother and the kids were out of the house and
the uncle tied up her feet with a belt. Then her
father sat on her and beat her across the face, curs-
ing her, saying, "Nigguh lover, nigguh fucker, you
only fuck for love, huh? You're crazy, I don't recognize your face any more. You don't look like you."
She tells me all the things he swore at her as he beat

her. "You're killing your mother and you're killing me." And "Whore, nymphomaniac." And "You should never have married him." She's afraid to answer back. She claims to have all the time been reciting "Om, om, om" to his face and slapping hands and then she switched to "Our father who art in heaven hallowed—" She says she thought he was killing her and she was dying. Meanwhile she says the uncle ran around turning over furniture making it look like a struggle. And her father is saying, "We've got a bed prepared for you at the hospital and a doctor will give you an injection." They untie her and the police come. She reads the police something from some Eastern book, about being in good humor. Then she asks to call her lawyer. Take her away, her father says. She's hysterical, psychotic. Well, I got myself together, she says, and was very calm. I wouldn't have been able to hold out if I hadn't had a bowl of brown rice before it all happened. Very calmly I told the cops I knew my rights and wanted to make a call. I called my lawyer in New York. I told the cops what he told me, that if they tried to take me in, I'd swear out a warrant for my father's arrest on charges of assault and battery and sue the city for false arrest. One of the cops was upstairs listening to my end of the phone conversation. He must have thought I sounded like I was telling the truth. So everyone backs off. The cops leave. I start to pack. Then my mother comes back

from this little drive she took with the kids and my
aunt. She wants to know why I'm leaving. He *beat*
me, Mother. He sat on top of me and beat me. Look
at my face. So she faints. I left with the kids. Tommy
was really confused. How come we're leaving? I told
him my father beat me, that he was nasty to me,
that he hit me. . . . That's her story. Is it true?
Exaggerated? The details sound right. It sounds
like her father. . . . I have no parents any more. I
can never go there again, she says. He tried to put
me in a mental hospital and take away my kids.

Sunday. After being with the kids for the day,
taking them up to a friend's house in Rockland
County, and being outdoors with them, nervous myself, answering questions and bringing people up-to-
date.

I take the kids back to Paula. My old apartment.
No electricity. Small candles burning here and there.
Fixtures and furniture gone. Pads and blankets on
the floor, piles of suitcases. Dimly lit rooms. A
mangy-looking spotted dog. A cat. Six or seven people lying around, some talking about how they were
gassed at Fort Dix in the afternoon, and how brave
they were. A fat loudmouth who calls himself a
Weatherman says he fainted and had to get mouth-
to-mouth before coming to. He tells of fighting with
a soldier, ripping off the soldier's gas mask and

punching him, then catching the spray directly in
the face. "I'm a black belt and I hit him pretty
hard." In the living room, a shambles. I sit and
talk with Billy, the old toothless black man she
brought up to my apartment a few days ago. He
is eating a bowl of noodles. He's got no socks on,
just shoes. He's vague. I try to get him on Esalen
when he tells me he worked there for years. Talking
with him is like talking to a crazy person. His brain
is burned out. Paula comes in and gives some black
guy named Jack a few stalks of something to cut up.
She shows him how to cut it. This living room once
had a rug, clean furniture, books on the wall, music,
happiness, light, pictures and posters. Now it smells
like a gymnasium, homeless castoffs lay around in
it, and a madwoman who was once my wife presides
over the mess, queen of the garbage heap. I wonder
if she even knows how much she enjoys seeing the
pain on my face when I'm here. I am containing so
much inside me that I feel novocain-numb.

I follow her through the dining room–study
where they're laying around on the floor, four or
five of them. Cushions and bed-packs everywhere. I
tell her we must go out. That I have to speak words
with her, but that I cannot find my tongue here.

Finally, we go out.

She doesn't want a beer. She wants to sit on a
park bench. I give her the seventy-five-dollar weekly

check. I ask her what's happening with the kids.
Are they getting fucked up? Are they interfering in
your life? No, no, I take them everywhere with me.
The people at the house are nice to them, she says.
Do you spend any time with the kids? I ask. Tommy
says you don't play with him or read him stories
any more. Sometimes yes, sometimes no, she says.
They need privacy. They need private times. Privacy? I ask. In that house?

I grope. What is it exactly I want to say. Casey
stirred something in me, something that I want to
express, but what?

She complains about her lawyer. We walk north
along Riverside Drive. I'm going to fire my lawyer,
she says. They're milking you, Jesse. They know
you've sold a book to the movies and they're just
taking you for a ride. All this time and we've ac-
complished nothing with these two lawyers, she says.
I want to sue you for a divorce, she says. Mental
cruelty. I lived with you all those years and I want
half the money. I supported you in many, many
ways that you probably don't know while you wrote
your books. I typed manuscripts for you. I'm entitled to something.

I am not giving you war reparations, I say. If you
had to put up with my craziness I had to put up
with your craziness as well. You wanted your in-
dependence and took it in this strange way so go

assume some responsibilities. You think you can just
indulge yourself and dig the scene and live off me?
I'll go to jail or burn the money or give it away
before I support that scene in the apartment.

Still walking north. About 112th Street and Riverside Drive.

What do you want me to do? Work? A job? I
work. I paint, I draw, I make clothes. I look after
the kids.

The kids are filthy. They stink from piss and their
clothes haven't been off their backs in days and
Suzie's hair is all knots. But I don't tell this to Paula.

You want some stranger looking after them? she
shouts. I need to stay home and take care of them.
I'm not going to work. You don't have a job. You
hated it. So why should I work?

I will give you money for the kids, no more.

She gives me the finger and turns away.

What kind of a plan do you have? she demands.
What are the magic words? Tell me. Say it. What
did you want to talk to me about because so far
you've told me nothing.

I tell her I am in despair. I go naked.

You're afraid, she shouts. You're a fool and a
hypocrite. Tommy wants you to have a life. Have
you ever asked if I'm okay, if I'm happy?

She kisses me on both sides of the cheeks. You're
like my father, she says. You want to control me still.

Do something productive, she mimics. What's the product? What shit!

How about a third person to talk with both of us, I suggest as a way out.

No. She shakes her head.

Not even a really good shrink?

No. I've had it on the past. It's the present I'm interested in. Nissim's my shrink. I love him. I'm going to have his baby. ("Am going to" or "may have"—I forget which.)

Eat the food, she says. Change is everything. That's what it's all about.

Why are you still so angry at me? I ask.

Good night, she says. There's nothing else to say. I don't know what this little talk was supposed to be about.

In the taxi going back I admit to the driver that I talked with my ex-wife and what we were talking about doesn't make any sense. I tried, I told him. But I didn't know what I wanted to say.

Nissim, Nissim. Her Tunisian prince. Supposed to come from a royal family back there. Was a junkie for six or seven years, she said, and she's been keeping him off it with a lot of brown rice. Paula met Nissim in June at a macrobiotic food lecture and stayed away until five o'clock that morning. Two weeks later we were separated. He's been living with her on and off since. Very emaciated guy with a big, bushy beard. Wears work clothes and boots. She replaces me with an Arab junkie. God!

After the next day's session I called the shrink Casey told me about. He sounded very nice. He said he had a busy, tight schedule, but that he thought one of his colleagues had room. A woman. He would call her for me. (I told him my story, in brief, on the phone.) I promised to call him tomorrow.

When I got home I checked Paula's story about what happened at her house in Pennsylvania. I called her father.

"I gave her a couple of whacks. Should have done it a long time ago." He won't be any more specific than that, and brushes off my questions about details.

"I wash my hands of it, Jesse. It's all up to you. Those kids will have TB and hepatitis in no time. They were so filthy when she was here. I gave them both baths. The water was black. They stank. Their clothes stank. She stank. She brought no clothes for them to change into. So if you think they're okay, then it's okay with me. But I'm not going to raise them, Jesse. And I'm not going to be driven crazy or kill myself in the next few months. It's up to you. I wash my hands of Paula. I'm done

with her. See the rabbi. See your lawyer. Work it
out. But leave me out."

He hangs up.

Sleeping is entertaining. It has its rewards. I meet
the unexpected. I fight. I run. I meet interesting
people. Guests from long ago drop by. I have strange
adventures. While it is happening, it is real enough.
I am disappointed with how drab my morning is in
comparison. Sleeping and dreaming is more romantic, more interesting, more everything than real life.

Night is no more worry, no decisions, no risks, no
further possibilities of trouble. Silly as this sounds, I
feel I must be repairing in my head because I am
able to think and write in sentences when from April
to June I could not make my pen write on a page.
At night I am more relaxed. I may go to a movie.
Have dinner with some girl who I make a pretense
with, or stay home and read. I never used to write
at night, but now I do—sometimes—like tonight.

I don't so much go to sleep as hibernate. I fall
asleep easily, too, unlike that time back last spring
when I averaged about three hours' sleep a night
for two or three months. The things that tortured
me then still torture me now, only now I deal with
it by giving myself some shots of emotional novo-
cain. I give myself a large dose to get to sleep.
Since I can't bear to repeat for the seven thousandth

time all my disasters, defeats and bad memories
and fears, I just turn them all off and go to sleep.
It is in a fairly numbing state that I go to sleep—
memory, desire, imagination, emotion under lock.
Only sleep opens it up. And I know I can survive
sleep, and even enjoy it. At least it is *something*
to look forward to.

Within five minutes I am asleep these days. Since
I enjoy sleep so much I let myself approach it with
real pleasure. Blackness. The deep comfort of the
pillow, its softness. The two sheets, above and below
me. It all engulfs me. I quietly welcome the on-
coming nothingness. I welcome the feeling of im-
pending oblivion. Quiet deaths and morning awak-
enings. I am in dreams where my pants don't fit in
the waist and the tailor declares them beyond re-
pair. My brother has stitches across his neck. There
are fields. I am shooting at someone—a girl. She is
pregnant. . . . I am in bed with my best friend's
wife. I am caressing her. She suggests I eat her. But
then I see someone sitting in the corner watching
us. I can't tell if it's him. It strikes me as one thing
to be nude in bed with her in his presence, whether
it's her husband or another man, but another to
engage in the kind of thing she suggests. There's
more but I don't recall what. Pretty soon there is
a lost dog in the room, a big male German shepherd.
Whenever I try to get close to see his tag, or take
hold of him so I can read the number, he bites into

my hand, not breaking the skin, but pinching and uncomfortable nonetheless. I see that in addition to the ASPCA tag there is an address tag, but when I try to read it his jaws increase their pressure. But what became of this dog and me, how I progressed in bed with my best friend's wife, whether I killed the girl with the rifle or fixed my pants, none of these do I find out. It is all left unresolved.

And when morning comes, and I see daylight, I am disappointed. My adventures are coming to an end. By staying in bed longer I hope to snatch a little more sleep and perhaps return to one of these episodes and discover a little more, round out the story, reveal myself to me through a fuller dream. But I never succeed, and I suppose the incompleteness of these dreams is significant, too.

I have no nightmares when I sleep. Only when I am awake. With the passing of the blessed dark hours I begin to perspire. I know when it is getting light. The longer I fight getting out of bed the more I sweat. If I get up at eight I am much drier than if I get up at eleven o'clock. Facing the world means being the perpetual witness to the crime upon myself, to the childless father, the unwriting writer. I am told by some people it is about time I recover from my recent troubles. Some people swear I have made great strides. But I think it's no longer a question of recovery. Can I ever care again? I don't care I don't care. I miss my children, I go to antiwar rallies, I keep the appointments with my shrink, I walk my dog, I make a semblance of caring for the girl I see. I do not accept my present reality except that I can hold my breath and not smell it and not be disgusted by it.

When it all happened last spring, and I went down to near-death, I found I didn't know what I really believed about anything, that I had no beliefs really. That I had possibly lived some kind of charade in her company, unafraid with her around, and without her petrified. I could have done anything: chased her through the halls of justice, taken the kids and gone off with them, gone away around the world myself, moved to a different city or another county, joined an expedition. But no. With all the freedom I could find nothing I wanted to do. Every little detail of my life became a colossal effort—laundry, writing checks, the bank, getting food. Mail went unanswered. I became catatonic. I ceased allowing myself things. I went away, me, the person I used to know. And the person who took my place was disintegrating.

The days are a carry-over of that awful time. Morning brings me into a wheezing, coughing fit. Not having smoked cigarettes in ten years and now smoking two packs a day. Sitting around and plucking hairs from one's scalp and dropping them on a table and wondering how many hairs it would take, falling together, before they produced a sound upon striking the wood. Now they fall only noiselessly, each day hundreds of individual hairs. Maybe five hundred hairs rolled into a bunch would make a sound when it struck the surface, a very soft sound, but louder than a feather would make, yet so soft that when the plucked, dead hairs landed, no one else would hear it, certainly no one who wasn't there in the same room watching and listening.

Madness at thirty-three to go to your parents and ask questions about their past, to request an accounting, resolve problems unresolved twenty-five years ago. We had dinner and then sat on high-legged upholstered chairs in the living room, at least ten feet between each of us. Ruben's answers to everything: "They didn't happen," or "You're exaggerating," or "Sure, so I had a temper, so what?" or "I was worried about making a living."

Listen, just listen and just pretend I'm not crazy, I want to know, all the time I was growing up in this crazy house, why did you suffer so, why your torment, your worried face, your silence, your anxiety, your vomiting attacks in the bathroom: what *was* all your suffering about? What were you so worried about? What kept you going during all that suffering? What kept you going? Where were your satisfactions?

"What kept me going was raising two sons and

having a nice home and clothes for you boys and
camps and sending you through school. What worried me was making a living. You haven't been in
the business world. You weren't in it very long. I was
the only Jew in a Christian firm. I was frustrated.
I could have been an officer in that company, but
they didn't promote a Jew that way. I stayed a
salesman. I *made* Howard Parks. And I made John
Malone and Ed Burns, too. They wouldn't have gotten where they were in that company without me.
I always had to outproduce the others and be better
than the other salesmen. I brought in the most
amount of business."

Okay, another question. The pornography in your
drawer. Why did you keep pornographic pictures
and books and a rubber dildo behind your prayer
books and tephillin in your chest drawer? Why?

Oh, *that*. She laughs. You knew about that? she
asks. At first he looks confused. Well—. Is that stuff
still around? he asks. I know he is lying. He knows.
It was for entertainment, he says, for guests when
they came over. Adults. (My shrink thinks he used
it to masturbate over.) It was just a coincidence that
it was in the same drawer as that other stuff. *Other
stuff?* It's not hypocritical, he says in rebuttal. Or especially odd.

How about attacking mother with a knife and
screaming on Yom Kippur that you would splatter
her blood with that knife all over the kitchen walls

because you thought she washed her stockings on
Yom Kippur? "You had a dream. *What?* I *never* did
such a thing." Amazing. Neither of them remember
it. They both deny the event. So far as they are concerned it is a figment of my imagination. Both the
perpetrator and intended victim take the same line.

How could you sit at a Passover table and wish
Ben a cancer? Your exact words: "I wish your son
gives you a cancer the way you're giving me one!"
He was wearing a long face and cutting up a little.
It got you mad.

Again, he doesn't recall the incident.

Why should he? There were so many. He doesn't
know which ones I remember, which ones made
more of an impression than the others.

Attacking me with a knife when I had packed a
bag and was taking an apartment in Stamford,
Connecticut, because I worked the night shift at a
radio station there, the hour drive back on the highway too tiring, my having been to college away for
four years, in the Navy, in Europe, and at twenty-
three, unhealthily living with them in the apartment
I'd lived in since I was five. She called him home
from work, the day before Passover. At two o'clock
in the afternoon you storm in the front door, rush
into the kitchen for a long cutting knife, screaming:
"Over my dead body will you leave this house today.
You think you're some kind of genius. Try it. Try
it! I'll make this the goddamnest Jewish tragedy

New York has ever seen. The newspapers will write
about it." I thought of rushing you and ending it
there, one way or another, you or me. But I didn't.
You threatened, also, to go up to the radio station
if I left, "behind your back," to tell them what a
bastard I was, to make a stink up there. Why? Why
did you take a knife to me? Why did you threaten to
kill me? For what?

"Well, you didn't live in a proper way. You just
packed a bag without saying anything before. It
wasn't proper to do something that way. Besides,
there must have been something more to it at the
time. Ever since you went away to college there was
a change in you. You used to be different."

To which Mother adds: "Yes, it wasn't right the
way you just packed and said you were leaving. It
wasn't right, it wasn't proper."

They both sit there, ten years later, in their living
room.

I want to shout at them. Nothing will penetrate,
though. What's done is done. I was wrong. I was and
still am the cause of their woes and anguish.

"Besides," he says, "didn't you ever show your
temper? Don't other people have tempers?" Mother
backs him up. "Dad has a temper. That's his nature,
that's his make-up. He always had a temper."

But *knives!* I shout. Threatening with intent to
kill. Over what? Making me a prisoner? Passover?

And now they see nothing wrong or odd about it
either.

The shrink calls it *amazing dissociation.*

The old reb in the Bronx you used to go to in times
of crisis and disaster. Was he the one person in your
life you talked to? What were those visits to the old
reb all about?

Oh, Rabbi uh what's-his-name, Rubie?

Ruben: He was a friend of my father's From the
same village. At holidays and time of trouble, I'd go
to him and he would say a prayer. We didn't talk.
Just he would say a prayer. And I would give him
a donation.

What do you mean why didn't we talk about sex?
We didn't feel it was proper. We weren't brought up
that way. Locking the bathroom door? Privacy.
What do you mean you never saw us naked? We
weren't brought up that way, Mother says. We had
all these brothers and sisters. Sex is personal, a private matter. When I saw *The Killing of Sister
George,* it made me sick to my stomach. I had to
leave.

You never talked to me. You were so worried, so
grief-stricken-looking. You gave off nothing but fear
and tension. Religion was like all the pills you take.
You put a Band-Aid on the cut periodically. The cut
stayed. The Band-Aids were always there.

What was your suicide attempt that time? Why
did you want to throw yourself off the George

Washington Bridge? Why did you have to send Ben
out to follow him? *What?* Oh come on now. She
laughs, Oh *that*. Yes, *that*. I must have . . . we had
a fight, and she stayed away the afternoon. That's
right, I went to my sister's house and he had to give
you children supper and put you to bed. . . . And
that's why you wanted to kill yourself and took all
your papers out of the chest and stuffed them in your
pocket? That's reason for killing yourself? My father
puffs on a cigar and shrugs. He is retired now.
Nothing bothers him. "I don't remember. It was so
long ago." Nobody remembers anything. Except me.

Why don't you remember the good things, Jesse?
What good things? You were a happy child, she
assures me. Only till six months, I answer. No, he
came up here to smear dreck on us, he says. No, to
talk, to ask you who you are. What did your father
do? Who was your mother? Tell me about them.
Why were they a secret?

My father was a presser. We had a dairy in Mas-
peth. He only worked half the year. He didn't do
anything when he wasn't pressing. He only helped
out a little in the dairy. I was the one who helped
my mother the most in the dairy. Lifting those big
milk containers at eight years old. She was the busi-
nessman, my mother. My father didn't help much.
I didn't like that. He was very dictatorial. About
religion and about everything. Toward the end of
his life he mellowed. He died four months before

you were born. Mother died the day before you were born.

Ah-hah! Was it *my birth* or your *mother's* death? A child born and you sit shiva through the pregnancy and after my birth. He sat shiva while I was coming. And he sat shiva for the death during and after my birth. He recited prayers for the dead, prayers of mourning while my life was starting. I am involved in the death of his parents. Thank you for finally letting me in on it.

As for love, we gave you plenty of that, she assures me. Never, I say. You were incapable of it. All you did was fight with him and take his shit and not talk to each other for half of every month as long as I remember. You screamed at each other. For days and weeks you wouldn't talk. You gave Ben and me messages. We would carry messages back and forth between you. At dinner the clink of silverware. No talking. Silence. Aggravation. Deadly sour looks. Now tell me about feeling love while this was going on.

Did you ever talk to me about your work? Well, no. But you worried about it, right? Look, I had to work damn hard to send you boys through school. You don't appreciate that. At the time I was only making . . . Money, money, money. It all goes back to that. What about the people you lived with? What about giving something of yourself? To show who

you are? You forgot something. You forgot to talk
to us. You forgot to respond to us.

A whitewash. It was all appearance. Accuse me
of something. I accuse you.

You had a job through the depression. You worried about it when you had a secure job. For twenty-
four years. Why didn't you change jobs if you didn't
like the company of goyim? It was a Jewish industry, textiles. Why did you choose to stay working
for a goy company? Why?

I didn't know the company would collapse a year
before my pension was to start. The years I worked
for them were the happiest days of my life.

Besides, I don't care any more; he says. I haven't
got long to go.

You've been on the fringes of death your whole
life long. Morning. Despair. Depression. A lifelong
death trip. You never once missed lighting a candle
for the dead. Did you ever light a candle for the
living? You prepared for death by avoiding life. Did
you start making preparations for your own death
when your parents died?

If you believe in an afterlife, he says, I hope
you're happier with your next parents. He smiles.
She laughs. Oh stop talking like that, she says.

You are forever giving me the keys to your vault
and safety deposit box in the event of your death.
You always remind me of your coming death. You

threaten suicide and you don't recall why. You threatened her with a knife and you don't remember the incident. You hold a knife under my nose and you say it's because there was something I didn't do properly. That's not a temper. That's psychotic. That's crazy rage. You admit to nothing. Why do you think I can talk to you now when I never could? You're still lying to yourself and to me. What are you afraid of? What are the secrets? What are you afraid someone might find out? That you're really crazy? Well, so is everyone else! Let it out: here's the secret, everyone is crazy, everything thinks he's crazy. You're just like everyone else.

What did you ever think of me? Were you ever concerned with anything except how things looked? You claim you were a successful salesman. You must have been an extrovert on the job, telling jokes and hustling. And then you come home and scream at the people living upstairs for making too much noise and throw milk bottles in the hallway and they call the cops in the middle of the night—during the happiest days of your life? Even now as I talk to you, you shrug and say it was all because you wanted to make a living. And clothe us and clothe Mother properly. And feed us. Grieving was what you were doing. For the dead in the synagogue and for the dead in the home. But for life? For the living, nothing.

Did they ask about my suicide? No, I brought it
up. I tell them I meant to do it. He only threatened.
"Oh stop," she says, "please don't talk that way."
Listen, face it in the eye. All you've done tonight is
shrug it off and sweep it under the carpet, as though
it is trivia. You don't know how to be honest. It's a
sickness. You avoided me as though I was a boarder.
You fed me and exhibited me and clothed me and
sent me to camps. But did you deal with me? Talk
to me? You taught me that the world was a terrify-
ing place. Look at the panic I saw in you all those
years. Panic. Why else did I feel panicky all those
years, at twelve and thirteen and fourteen, wondering how I would make a living, who would take care
of me, not feeling I was complete, preparing for the
grown-up world of panic. What else did I know? I
saw it only through your panicky eyes, the money,
the goys, the fear. Life was to be feared. Watch out.
Be careful. Don't overdo it.

As I say, my pleasure has been raising two sons,
and they're both successful and I'm proud of that.

As I say, in your next reincarnation I hope you
have parents you're happier with.

They are made of stone. They don't hear. They
don't feel.

As I start to leave they give me more vault keys
and the keys to their house as well, just in case anything happens. And she says: try to bring the chil-

dren up next weekend. She has heard nothing of my
anger. She is too used to his anger. It has all been
small talk. A passing conversation. When will we see
you again? Can you make it next Friday?

Paula, she says, must be made of stone, she must
have an iron constitution. I could never leave like
that with two children, she says. I couldn't walk out
on him just like that. Was Mother a virgin? I ask
him. Yes, he snaps. Did you have sexual experience
before you got married. Yes I did, he snaps.

We sacrificed plenty, she says. You boys always
came first. Some other parents take first for themselves and second for their children, but not us. You
always came first.

I treated Paula like you treated me, impersonally,
coldly, quietly.

She says: You make us feel awful. Like we were
the world's worst parents. That we did something
terrible to you. We gave you love. We gave you love.
We *gave you love*.

Did his father to him? Probably not. How far
does it go back? His great-grandfather? The villages
in Russia and Poland and Austria and Hungary and
Germany? The men who wrote the Old Testament?
Blame who?

You gave me no clue how the world worked. You
hid from the world all your lives. "What do you
mean? What did you expect us to do? If you want

to have some security in your old age you've got to
save and protect and you can't be running
around. . . ."

Jesse, she says, why didn't you ask us some of
these things when you were younger? Because. Because I didn't know the questions. I didn't know
what was bothering me. I didn't know the problem.
And because nobody ever talked to anybody in this
house. . . . Well, you can't live without money,
can you? There you are. That's your answer, she
says. See?

You said the same prayer words over and over and
you blotted out all the real world. You don't know to
this day what those medicine-man words mean. I—
I do too. Come on then, translate any line for me.
Get your siddur.

Death, money. He took me to the cemetery, took
me to the synagogue so I could stand beside him in
a suit while he grieved. Took me to a monumentalist
in New Jersey to pick out a stone for his dead—who?
The entire conversation conducted with their sitting
in easy chairs, at opposite ends of the room, me sitting on the sofa. Everyone was comfortable. I
shouldn't be doing this now. What does it accomplish? It validates my childhood? So I can validate
them? I have one foot in his world and one foot in
the other world. Some ways I am still his spitting
image. I was a shut-in. I would have been better off

growing up in a concentration camp. At least I'd
have known where I was at, what was happening.

    I tell it all to Nathanson. He breaks out laughing,
his first laugh, at my question to him about the pornography behind the prayer books.
    I can see your anger, he says, but they're not the
enemy any more.
    Who *is* the enemy then? *Is* there an enemy?

V

from notebook four

October 27. I haven't written in here for over a week. I've been retyping *Waiting,* and I have now finished it. I don't know if the book is a disaster, or unresolved, or a slow, boring mess, or a masterpiece, or a fear-struck, dreamlike account of a man whose life's problems are all catching up with him but who refuses to admit it. I really have no perspective on it.

I've finally paid fourteen hundred dollars in doctors' bills—to hospitals, to hand surgeons, to shrinks, to this one, that and the other. I still take taxis everywhere I go, back and forth to the Village, to Nathanson's. I hang on, irritated with him, with his cold way and my numbness that seems to start in more than ever when I enter his office. Through Casey's shrink I am now seeing this woman, Janet Ryder, at the same time I am seeing Nathanson. She belongs to the Sullivanian school. She is more talky, friendly, outgoing, and altogether a very different kind of shrink. We chat, whereas I agonize with Nathanson. She is calm, and kind, and warm. But keeping the schedules with both of them is a mess. Six appointments a week. I tell them much of the same material, and it's confusing as all hell. But since I can't decide between them, I see them both. I've already told them each that I am seeing the other. I am supposed to make up my mind soon or get dropped by each. Dropping the whole shitty psychoanalytic mess is also a possibility. Has it been doing me any good? I'm still alive. Janet deals a lot with my relationship with the kids. She hasn't quite gotten on to how flipped out Paula is, but I get tired of repeating stories. Sometimes, though, telling her the old stuff, it sounds different in the retelling.

Still sleeping late. Molly-dog is here with me now and she's been alone a lot. I don't take her for very long walks. I don't feel much about her being here.

Yesterday Paula's mother called from Las Vegas. Her husband kicked her out, she said. "We'll be dead in six months if we keep worrying like this," he said to me. "Get out of here." She had a scheme for me to come to Vegas with the kids and establish residence for forty-three days and put a notice in the paper and twenty or thirty days later I'll be divorced. Her lawyer-nephew out there, an assistant DA, explains the details, all about the Nevada divorce laws. Then she gets back on the phone and tells me horror stories about seeing a loved one mistreat loved ones, how dirty the kids were, Paula's irresponsible neglect, Tommy banging his head against the refrigerator when she won't feed him, Paula's "three husbands" story, and more horror stories.

Las Vegas! I gag. Another loony alternative. How can that whole family be so quick to turn on one of their own? It would make Paula mad-crazy for the rest of her life. They stayed on the phone with me for a half hour, trying all kinds of persuasion. I finally told them I would take it up with my lawyer.

I am now involved with a girl Bud sometimes went out with in Montreal and New York. A lawyer, Michele Hearn, bosomy, thirty, a civil rights, civil liberties freak. She has a pretty apartment on West 10th Street, for about ninety dollars a month. Just picked up the phone and called her one night.

We have wine and cheese and then go out to dinner. I tell her some of what's been happening. I see the pain in her face. "You keep coming back to it," she says. "It's all you can talk about. You're totally preoccupied with it."

She confesses that she blocked out Paula's name (she'd met her twice), how she's read all my books. She's calm, untroubled-seeming, wrapped up in social and political affairs. Abortion law reform is her

current big case. Also some stuff about getting SDS
kids out of jail. She's been involved with the Movement for years.

We discuss Bud. She's a little mysterious about
her relationship with him. But she isn't really a mysterious girl. She keeps telling me she liked me, liked
the person, liked the memory, loved my books.

On her couch, after coffee, we neck. She has to
get up early to go to work. Okay, I'm leaving. But
we keep necking. I get down toward her crotch and
feel the resistance. I'm ready to go. But she doesn't
seem to push the point hard enough. "Who did you
expect to find here? she asks. I didn't know, I tell
her. Someone who put me on to a great Sam Hinton
record two or three years ago. Someone named
Michele, with a plus sign, but wasn't exactly a
Michele and who I didn't really know.

"You're scaring the hell out of me," she says.

I assume she's referring to my scar, my depression,
my trembling when I kiss her—one of them.

But I continue, and even manage a joke, and she
says how nice, see? you can laugh. So we sleep together, two goes at three o'clock and then in the
morning. She doesn't like to be played with, groped.
I don't understand her reluctance there. No appar-
ant orgasm or real heat. We don't sleep much, a
couple of hours. Exhausted in the morning. She calls
the office and sounds official, telling the switchboard
girl she'll be late. We breakfast and ride uptown on

the bus. Can you make it for dinner Sunday night? she asks. I'm having some friends. Yes, yes.

She works with the biggest big-deal lawyers in the civil liberties field. She loves her work, fears trials, and has enormous breasts.

She's a straight head-on fucker. More domestic than she lets on, even though I call her "the eminent woman jurist." She smiles a lot, warmly, and I don't know how to respond, or what she means. I make it plain to her that I have been through a long, long dead-cold neuter phase and not to expect much. A numbness. I can't quite tell her I'm still in it. I don't think she believes me about the extent and depth of the paralysis. I believe Michele is one of the good people of the world.

I see her again Sunday night, after the kids. A great dinner (she's a marvelous cook) : wine and artichokes and saucy chicken and apple pie. Talk with her sociologist friends who are going off to Jamaica, a field trip. After a while they leave and we make love. Am I her stud now? I don't feel much about all this, except that I know I'm getting little hand squeezes from her, pecks, warm smiles—to which I fail to react. She really seems to like me. I wonder why. I'm so unresponsive. She's so sweet and self-assured and competent.

Window bars next to the bed. Fire escape. The moon comes in. A romantic little apartment. Practical girl, Michele. Practical thinker, practical fuck.

Going to work in the morning after bacon and eggs.
This time the train. I go home to emptiness.

Tommy and Suzie over the next weekend. Picked
them up at 108th Street. Nissim in his underwear.
Paula looking tired, saying she's got to pack today.
She shows me her new Astrakhan winter coat. I tell
her I'll be back at six with Suzie. Tommy will stay
with me overnight. She doesn't know that the day
before I talked with Mrs. Haines, director of the
nursery school Tom went to last year, where he's
gone a little bit this year. Mrs. Haines told me how
Tommy came into school pain-faced and crying,
that Paula didn't take him into school but sent him
in from the car by himself, that he seemed terribly
upset this year, that this elderly black man picked
him up, that at first she couldn't get Tommy to even
talk to her, and that the teacher said the longer he
sat on her lap the less the crying got. Last time he
was there, she said, he made a beautiful wooden air-
plane, really worked hard at it with sandpaper and
saw. She said she thought he must be undergoing a
lot of strain but that he seemed pretty sturdy.

Back to my place and they are delighted to see
Molly. She gives them big, big licks. We go to the
park and then to the old neighborhood, to the Piersons, where Tommy plays with Jim, his old buddy,
and Suzie with Irene, the Rosenberg's kid. Talking
with neighbors. Kids building with blocks, fooling
around. Barbara comes over. Suzie naps. Dinner.
Time to go back. Barbara comes with me. She will

finally meet the famous Paula she's heard so much about. But she's not there. We wait downstairs a half hour. Then head back to my place. I make hamburgers. Tommy starts in about meat and killing cows and how afraid cows must be right before they're killed. Barbara throws me an upset look. I still can't reach Paula. I keep calling. No one home. Why is she doing this? It's eight o'clock, two hours past when I said I'd bring Suzie back.

Suzie has bad diarrhea. I've changed her three times and now I have no more pampers. We get down on the floor and play "Battling Tops." Tommy wins a few but Barbara is pretty good and she wins some and pretty soon Tommy loses interest. I put Suzie to sleep. She stinks something awful. I've got no bed, or diapers, or clothes for her. Barbara leaves at ten. Paula is still not home. Suzie sleeps on a rug, on cushions, her ever-present pacifier in her mouth, bucking her teeth. Barbara looked like she couldn't stand it any more; probably I seemed very upset and anxious. I read to Tom and then he goes to sleep. What did I feed Suzie? Bananas and yoghurt.

Next morning we walk the dog after breakfast. Then look for pampers. While we're gone Molly tears the garbage up all over the living room rug. Suzie is screaming. She's filthy and wet. I put a dry diaper on her and the pair of pajamas I had bought for Tom. She goes to sleep. Tom and I play with the tape recorder. Finally, Paula gets home. "I lost my purse. I was out in Staten Island at a lamasery cele-

brating the equinox and there was no phone. You
can bring them up now."

A strange dream. I am in school trying to study
for a math test for which I am unprepared. A hip-
looking girl shows me a copy of *Art News* with a
special section on pornography in the back. Later in
the dream I am in a car—a jeep—going to a baseball stadium. In the jeep is a Marine driver, a Chinese doctor, and me and the girl in back. The teams
are a conventionally uniformed baseball squad and a
team of long-hairs, in bell-bottoms, shuffling around.
The girl roots for the latter, the two in front (we are
parked behind some netting, looking down into the
stadium) root for the straight team. I root for neither. We leave, drive off. Soon we drive back. When
we get there it has rained, the players are gone, the
field is wet and muddy, the stands empty, the whole
place deserted.

We carry an enormous history around inside us.
We forget chapters. We remember chapters. Mostly
we forget chapters. That's why it makes so little
sense.

I keep on going to the two shrinks at the same time.
I confess to you, paper. No one else knows. Not even

Michele. Of the dream, Janet suggested my fear of
failure, of not being able to live up to certain standards (math tests everyone pass), being back in school
meaning that I have always felt unsuccessful and inadequate. Between the two of them, Nathanson and
Ryder, they find the important part that I stood
outside the ball game, watching the straight team
in uniforms and the hip team in old clothes and that
I am merely curious, not siding with one or the other.
Then we left and when we came back there was
desolation and emptiness. I had made no choice, and
now I was even deprived of that choice. Between
one and the other, I stood indecisive and chose neither. As a result, I got desolation.

You envy your brother's worldliness, says Janet.

Was your brother good in math? says Nathanson.

Was there ever any way you could please your
parents? asks Nathanson. No, no way.

Janet: Your parents were disapproving people.
They discouraged any attempt at your becoming independent of them.

I make a half-hearted attempt to tell Nathanson
I don't like him.

Molly spends such long hours here alone on the
nights I spend with Michele.

Paula has moved and will not say where she is
living, where she has gone with the kids. Someplace

on 6th or 7th Street. I won't send her any dough
until she says where she is living. A telephone call to
her mother: she has the address. I write her.

I tell her that when I'm lonely for Tom I'd like
to be able to pick up the phone and talk to him,
and would she please get a phone. I ask her to please
put him in school so he's not always hanging around.
I write quietly about his developing food hang-up
and his dreams of going to jail and disappearing
which have something to do with her drug bust and
her bravado about a coming political bust. I tell her
I feel desperate and plead with her to get things
together, and I admit to learning about how crippled I've been. I try to say how it was with my
writing, how when an imaginary world and all its
people and problems take over the inside of your
head it becomes more important than the real
world, how I become its prisoner and slave, how I
forget flesh-and-blood people. Beautiful for art, but
a terrific crash-escape from the real world, to remove
oneself in some respectable way like that from dealing with the needs of others. I tell her of my images
of a little girl asleep on a cold floor in an unheated
room, her brother too, and her mother sitting out
front stuffing cotton into Molotov cocktails. I try
not to be preachy in the letter, or nasty, but honest,
recalling stuff, able to talk to her in print as I can't
in person these days.

If, as Hesse says, you seek only your own fate, then you are lonely forever.

Does one ever reach home? *Is* there such a thing as home? Or do we get tired looking and settle on a place, rent it for life?

After a weekend of watching TV, I went out and bought a TV.

Could it be that my awful morning depression business ("Oh God, not *another* day") is a result of the suicide, still thinking that I shouldn't be waking up from sleep? Or that sleep itself I find a little suicidal, a chance for temporary oblivion, and I am irritated with having to make the effort when I discover each morning that I am still "in life."

Spent the weekend with Michele. Saturday late afternoon there for dinner. I took Molly with me. A strange, slow, dull weekend. We had wine and cheese and then steak and went to see an awful

movie, *Marry Me, Marry Me*. And all the time I was
at Michele's Molly wouldn't shit because she had no
grass. Only when you have a grass-addicted dog do
you realize how little grass there is in the Village.
Late movie on TV Saturday night. Raining outside.
Lazy. Nothing Sunday. Just sat around doing nothing. She wore a robe all the time. She uses hand
cream. I tell her too many Paula stories. With her
I always try to make singulars out of plurals, very
self-consciously. "We were in . . ." "When we went
to . . ."

Michele still doesn't know about the two shrinks.
Yet she has said, in general, that she feels my pre-
vailing indecisiveness is appropriate.

One day in November I took Tom and Susan to
the Bronx Zoo. Michele borrowed a car from a
friend for the trip. Tom giggling over the monkeys,
Suzie laughing about the roaring tiger. Michele was
a little uncomfortable when Suzie cried in her arms.
I would pass Suzie over to Michele every now and
then when my left wrist started hurting too much
from carrying her, and I bought lots of presents—
parrot dolls, stuffed dogs, things you squeeze and
make jump.

When it started to drizzle, Tommy said "Let's
split." He also told some fuzzy stories about some
"pigs pulling a gun on Nissim" someplace upstate
when they stopped to watch a rainbow. Back at the

apartment played "Battling Tops" and hiding games.
Suzie came out of her shell a little to play some of
the hiding games. I'd hide under a bed, in a closet,
behind a chest—and they'd have to find me. Then
we'd change hider and finder. Suzie thought it was a
riot, smiling coyly. Paula received them at the Para-
dox Restaurant, the macrobiotic restaurant on 7th
Street. Tommy, Suzie and Paula all had diarrhea.
Paula went on about her drug rap. She would cop a
misdemeanor plea, as her lawyer suggested, because
then she'd get a suspended sentence and be out on
parole and since she was sure she was going to be
arrested on a political rap later in the year, she didn't
want that hanging over her head. Instead, she said,
she'd fight the felony rap on the grounds entrapment
was unconstitutional, even though it was contrary to
her lawyer's advice. And she told me how she's been
embezzling traveler's checks. She buys them, gives
them to a friend with her identification. Her friend
forges her signature and then cashes them. Paula reports them lost and then collects from the company,
showing them the receipts and thus collecting twice.
Why are you doing it, Paula? They've got too much
money, the capitalist pigs. Yeah, but you can get
caught—and that's not even a political offense. I'm
careful, nah. Paula drove me over to Michele's street,
where I got drunk on wine with Michele, requested
some music, and we balled all over the living room
to the Beatles.

At a friend's party with Michele, the night before. All Fire Island people. I had a first-rate near-
fainting anxiety attack. Not sure why. Wife of a
friend coming on to me, swearing her love, tugging
gently on chest hairs protruding over my shirt, telling me about letters she wrote me and didn't mail.
Agent Elaine a little soused and kissy, telling me how
fantastic my new book is, the most brilliant thing
to cross her desk in years, that it was so good it made
her uncomfortable.

To Washington, November 15, in a rented car
with Michele. Moratorium—New Mobilization
March on Washington, five hours' drive down the
New Jersey Turnpike. In the rain. To a hotel off
17th and N.
Thinking of hotels I'd stayed in with Paula.
Never saw so many people, together in one place,
in my life. Spotlights glaring on candle-carrying,
war-dead readers marching in front of the White
House. We had dinner in an Arab restaurant. To
Dupont Circle after, seeing the broken glass on the
sidewalk, smelling the sharp smell of lingering tear
gas.
Saturday, cold as hell. Endless marching. Thou-

sands of parade marshals, jumping up and down to
keep warm. Up Pennsylvania Avenue, NLF flags,
New Jersey contingents. Michele looking for people
she knew, finding some. Everyone freezing but feeling good. At the monument, another hundred thousand already gathered, in blankets and sleeping bags,
applauding speeches and singers. McGovern; Good-
ell; Dave Dellinger; Pete Seeger; Peter, Paul &
Mary; the cast of *Hair*. Begging Hare Krishna people exploiting the crowds. We wandered, footsore,
cold. A terrific feeling of solidarity. Walked to a hotel lobby for coffee and then over to the Justice Department where we saw more kids pull the flag down
at the IRS building and then fight for it, a war
trophy—wrestling and rolling and punching on the
ground. Suddenly some windows were smashed and
the crowd got jittery. Minutes later a barrage of
tear gas came looping down the street directly into
the crowd, maybe twenty smoking cans in all, a
graceful arc. A moment of panic. "Walk, walk,"
went the chant. We did, fast. "Free Bobby Seale,"
chanting. Crowd-dispersal gases work. Coughing and wheezing and sneezing. A lot of kids in gas
masks and helmets. Cops started pushing us back
down the street. We barely got out. Michele looking
a little sick from the drifting gas. I was exhilarated,
trembling with excitement. I wanted to stay. "On
to the White House," the cry went up. Visions of

barricade-storming and tall ladders, the French Revolution, Russian Revolution, American Revolution.
    The hotel. Memories of hotels with Paula, all
over the world, especially Israel. A breakfast room
in this place like many Israel hotels. Checked out
and went to the Kennedy grave site, the city empty-
ing out. Where and how all the people evaporate?
At Arlington, my throat chokes when I see the
burning light. Does it choke for Kennedy? Or for
me? I remember what I was doing that day when he
died, interviewing someone at NBC, in another life,
quietly married, in 1963, living on West End Avenue,
Paula teaching in New Jersey, Chet Huntley coming
crying down the hall, gathering notes for my first
novel, just back from Israel and putting together
that Israel book, and no children yet. Oh God. Oh
God. Only married three years. My stomach flops
and panics. Free-lancing then. Oh God. The flutters
in my stomach. How long ago. Yet it was my life.
How does all this make sense? Where is everything?
Who is this girl? For a moment I think I am going
to faint. My bowels churn. My heart dies a little
more, saddened and pulled down. I've lost it all, everything I worked so hard for. In the car driving
around the city, looking, my mind going and going.
Lincoln Memorial. Pentagon, paint on the Justice
Department walls, giving V-signs to black soldiers
who return the V-sign. On out of the city to the
highway, trying to plug up a leak in the air vent.

Legs freezing. Would this be a convenient car to use? Michele talks on and on. I glance over occasionally, not often, half expecting to see a redhead next to me. North we go, everyone on the road—just like when we came down—bearded, sloganed, longhaired, bumper-stickers for peace. A cold, hard, bright blue fall day out. God, how I hate the fall, how much fear and unknown in the pit of my stomach in falls past. I tell Michele why I hate the fall, reviewing every desperate, despondent fall I can think of. I don't want the car ride to end. On Route 1, a giant sign: "Modess Because. . . ."

We return the car to Korvettes, 84th and Broadway.

November was Michele sleeping over here several times, on my soft, back-hurting bed, was Michele in bed with me when the kids woke up Sunday morning and found Daddy in bed with a new woman, and Tom made no comment, he climbed into bed, as did Suzie, and we played with them in bed, Michele putting on a bathrobe. Strange to see her in bed with my kids, strange to see Suzie on her lap, strange to see her reading to Tommy in bed. I resent it.

November was Tommy talking nostalgically of his past, the summers at the beach that he loved, his friends there, records we used to listen to but which his mother threw out, bike riding in Central Park, of a life that doesn't exist for him any more. Where are all my old friends from the park? he would ask. I never see them any more.

November 26 dream.

High school graduation. Mike Burnside in charge of getting the arrangements made in our dorm. Mood of hilarity and exaltation. I looked at a big filing cabinet in the room. Looked up my permanent school record. Saw a file, "Baby Jesse Jacobi wetting in kindergarten." Turned away and saw other kids smoking grass, Jerry Sandeman in particular. They were nude. Didn't join them immediately. I put it off—the fun—to do something else, to pack. I looked for a pipe, a strainer, in my locker in the room. I took a couple of tokes off their cigarette, but I didn't take off my clothes and sit on the floor with them.

I took sweaters and jackets out of the locker. Packing and unpacking always a big deal for me. There were dolls in my locker. A gray Windbreaker I wore when I was eleven or twelve.

While in the packing stage, my father came in and looked where I wasn't, down to the other side. I was an hour late in getting down to the ceremonies. I knew he and Mother were waiting. He said nothing and left.

I loaded the car with cartons of books. I saw

Brigit and asked her what happened. She didn't look
pregnant any more. I absorbed it, she said. Her
pretty sister was there, too.

I had two cars, both foreign. One red and the
other white, one I had been using, and the other,
the white, I hadn't. I loaded the white car. What
was the destination for this trip?

Two kids ran around the corner, nearly falling,
skidding in the turn, veering way over, off balance,
but they didn't fall down, they kept running.

November 24 dream.

Sam and Hilda accompanied me from Winston
Hospital when I had an evening pass. They dropped
me off near the hospital on the way back. It was
night. It was farther from the hospital than I had
thought. The neighborhood was a bad one. It was
threatening. I was scared. A tall man with an odd
shirt came up to me. A mugger. I assumed he wanted
my watch and money. I was prepared to give them
to him. But he didn't ask for them. He rolled up a
towel with a knot in it and hit me with it. I reacted
by turning my head the other way. The thing didn't
hurt. He hit me with it three or four times, and it
still didn't hurt. That surprised me. He said the hell
with it.

He took me to a restaurant, a cafe, a brightly lit
place. We sat at a table. It was crowded. I didn't

resist or try to run away; why? At another table was
a kid I recognized from high school or camp. I only
recall his face. I don't recall his name. He was
neither a friend nor acquaintance. He was smiling
and happy; in fact, he was always smiling and
happy, that was my recollection of him. I inquired
about his older brother.

Next day I went back to the restaurant, which
was at Broadway and 110th Street now. I was supposed to identify the mugger to the police who
would meet me there. Crossing the street, a drunk
stopped me and said, "Help me cross the street and
I'll give you two dollars." I helped him across the
street and then couldn't decide whether to take the
two dollars or not. I did. I thought that I had been
robbed last night and needed the money, even
though I hadn't been robbed; all I had done was
worry about being robbed—the robbery never took
place. I saw four policemen at the restaurant. End of
dream.

—My feat was worse than the actual event. The
thief was kind, didn't hurt me, took me to a restaurant.

—Felt I had been deprived of something, in taking the drunk's money. But of what? Stealing, according to Janet, in stealing you want something,
want to get something that wasn't naturally forth-
coming in the first place, at home. Like love. Na-

thanson said, "Maybe you're afraid I'll take something away from you as well."

Where is my mother in all this? Janet wants to know. Where?

I tell her:

She gave me a bath till I was twelve.

She put sticky green paste on my hair to keep it down.

She never let me cook a meal or make a meal for myself the whole time I lived in that house with them.

She does the dishes immediately after dinner, as soon as the last spoonful of dessert is out of her mouth.

She's taking thousands of pounds of pills.

She would say "uh-huh" when I felt sick, put her lips to my forehead, say "uh-huh" again, as though, "I told you so," or "That's what happens when you don't listen, you get punished, you get sick."

Childhood recurring dreams:

—The falling through space, falling and falling and waking up before hitting bottom. (Terror, instability, insecurity, no one to hold me.)

—Holding my breath. Waking up suffocating, choking. I can't exhale, can't breathe out. I can't catch my breath. I gasp for air in terror and near-suffocation.

—The back of my father's closet. There's a dark tunnel there and it leads to a place outside, in Fort Tryon Park, above the playground where I played many times as a child. (The way out, suggests Janet, was somehow through my father's world, not my mother's.)

The two analysts go on and on. He says he will definitely discharge me at the end of the week if I haven't decided for myself by then.

My vacuum cleaner attachment broke.

Went to an anti-Nixon rally at the Waldorf. Flying wedges, high school children taunting horseback cops, girls screaming mother-fucking pigs, hoody-looking types wearing peace buttons pretending they're not cops. A distinguished-looking Wasp with an attaché case, about fifty, wearing a hat and a long overcoat: he passes a barricade and looks at the rabble. "You spoiled children," he says, shaking his head, moving on. If the cops weren't there the spoiled children would have killed him. "You go and get your balls shot off in Vietnam, mother-fucker," they scream.

Paula left a small book of poetry with me last time, about a divorced girl suffering in her remembering, lapsing into uncertainty, crying for herself and creating her own new present. In response I write Paula a rambling letter, like the last, poking around the past, re-evaluating and re-examining. And with criticism I compliment her on taking care of the kids. Why am I writing her these letters?

December 12.
Wrote Nathanson a letter. He asked me write him something about why I broke it off between us. Told him here he was a year younger than me and formally holding on to the Doctor-Mister thing, that I could never call him Jack. Mentioned the agonizing monologues, that there was little two-way communication, that trying to get my feelings out of dead storage couldn't get going when the shrink was so stolid and cold himself, that there was something about him and his ungiving way that paralleled my parents not giving out with themselves. Salt in an open wound. Said I didn't know if it was him himself, or the analytical situation he practices in. Thanked him for his patience and help and whatever else may have been happening that I didn't see.

I am detained, or robbed, and am held by the police. They escort me past a platform where Hitler is speaking. The man leading me says, "Ah, he's really not such a bad guy."

The next night, in the dream, the police keep
questioning me, asking for my identification. Suspicious. I feel punishment is imminent. They let me
go. But I know I am under surveillance.

Stories I tell Tommy: about a dog who helps a
squirrel who then helps the dog find food in a trash
barrel and how they become friends, how the dog
protects the squirrel and keeps other dogs from chasing the squirrel while he gathers nuts. . . . Some
similar theme in the knight going off looking to find
a dragon. When he finds the dragon it is sad because
its best friend, a donkey, is lost. The knight and
dragon go off to look for the donkey. They find it
bound up by some bad hunters, and together, knight
and dragon, they drive the hunters off. In both
stories the animals or heroes aren't supposed to be
friends but they *are* friends nonetheless.

A dream of Henry shooting my dog. She crumbles.
He is sitting on a chair near the ferry at the beach.
I hit Henry over the head with the gun. He is drunk.
I call the ASPCA. It is Sunday. I call the Coast
Guard. The question, and reason, for the calls:
what do you do with a dead dog on Sunday at the
beach?

I don't grieve for the dog and I don't really pur-
sue Henry. I am practical. I squash sentiment and
sit on emotion. I just want to make the arrangements. Does it mean I want the dog dead? Is she a
nuisance? Do I identify with Henry? I don't see my-

self really responding to what happened with her. I
handle the whole thing very formally.

December 15.
I turned on for the first time since last April.
I've been fucking to this stuff for the past week.
And listening to music. Coming up at night and going down in the morning. But at least the nights are
good. Before everything was the same, a monotone,
a gray inertness.

Since recommencing to smoke, I have, in the day-
time, decided between shrinks; wrote to my agent
about some work; decided to drive a taxi; discussed a
better separation agreement with the lawyer; talked
to M. more, screwed her better, understood her
more; slept with a girl named Sally; burned some
incense; didn't feel guilty about not fucking M. one
night when I slept with her.

Michele is dignified. That's her trouble. In almost
every respect she is the exact opposite of Paula. She
is rational, composed, she plans ahead, is thrifty, has
big tits, is dignified. She is ladylike, poised, controlled. She is a former Good Girl compared to
Paula's thinking of herself as a former Bad Girl.
Michele brushes her teeth at night and puts on cold
cream.

Michele is a former Good Girl, the kind who was
brought up properly and wouldn't screw, who used

to neck a lot in high school and college, repressed
the urges, felt you had to keep it till love or marriage, drove the boys (like me) mad. But Paula was
a Bad Girl, did it early, fifteen, and kept on doing it,
and couldn't say no. Michele could say no.

Michele: you can't give hand-jobs. You don't
know how to play with a cock and you've never
blown me. You tighten up when I journey south-
ward along your slopes to eat you. When I thought
of that, inside you, listening to the Jefferson Air-
plane, I went limp, wondering what music you made
love to last year, and with whom, remembering all
the rock music I smoked to and fucked to last year.
You were more involved with music for a longer
time than me, you said, and don't need grass to appreciate music (and make love good) like I do.
You're more levelheaded.

Having gone limp, I tell her all this. Thinking and
adding what's in it for her, what a strange girl. Do
I want to show her all that stuff? Is this one of the
things she wants to get from me? She's given *me* so
much. What has she gotten back? What do you
think about all this, Michele, now that I've told you
what's on my mind. I don't know, she says. You may
have hit the nail on the head. Or you may not: I
don't really know for sure. And later, you say,
"Jesse, do you want to teach me?" Or did you say,
"Jesse, you'll have to teach me," after I said, well,

you're affectionate but don't really know all the dirty, lecherous, sexy stuff and maybe you want to know about it. "But do I want to teach you?" I ask you. Yes and no. Yes because it's fun, and no because it might turn you into an insatiable mollusk.

Your breasts: well, they're a big subject. I have been avoiding them. "As though I were Paula," you say. So, playing with them Saturday night and Sunday night, a half hour on end. When I call my interest in them to your attention, you say, "Yes, I've noticed your interest as well as your past lack of interest." Well, having dealt with one woman for eight or nine years who felt titless, who didn't like them touched, I get into the routine of overlooking tits. Now, playing like a baby with yours, I ask myself, "Do girls really like having their tits played with? Really enjoy it? Or is it a supposed masculine thing to play with a girl's tits and consider it a big deal enough though a man derives no particular satisfaction, except the satisfaction of unconsciously recalling Mommy's tits." She laughs and laughs. "What do *you* think?" she asks. "Uh, I guess that, obviously, you enjoy it." You know some things about women, Jesse, but there's a lot you don't know. Didn't learn. Overlooked. Forgot.

An idea for a story, a book, a movie. WALK: a Radical women's rights organization, initials standing for Women Also Like to Fuck. That's what the

fight is all about. Having equal everything really
means women want equal orgasms. Michele snickers
politely and says the Women's Lib movement is
about more things than just that, grander issues.
Equal rights in general. Not just sex, she says. How
do you know, I ask, that that's not at the core of it?

The hero of the story—as opposed to the revolutionary gun-toting WALK heroine—is a psycholo-
gist studying sleep. A man totally caught up in sleep.
All he talks about during his conscious hours is sleep,
all he studies is sleep, all he thinks about is sleep.
The dream process, his dreams, others. A minute after he meets a new person he immediately starts
grilling him, or her, about his sleep habits. He gets
involved with the girl from WALK, who tells him
about her ex-husband, and he tells her about his ex-
wife, and neither of them relate to each other. Her
ex-husband turns out to be his ex-wife's present boyfriend. Or is that too much? Does the WALK girl
have to have been married?

Had some very creative thoughts under grass last
night. To respond creatively, to enjoy yourself sexu-
ally, to see and understand your life are all func-
tions that depression hasn't allowed to happen. That
it happens under grass means they're still there, that
they can return.

Cutting a tendon on your left hand's thumb in a
suicide attempt, he said, struggling with himself,

means that when you want to take off your pants
quick you have more trouble with the button. Very
honest.

Michele remarked on my stories about the knight
and the dragon, the dog and the squirrel, that I told
Tommy. They're not supposed to be friends in the
eyes of the world, she said. Who do they represent?
Me and Paula? Me and Michele? In whose eyes
shouldn't they be friendly? Natural enemies who end
up together.

The tape recorder. "Michele, I need a tape recorder to get all this down. It's important stuff to
me. Maybe it's life and death. I feel so much life tonight. I'm afraid I'll forget it all. The need to entertain myself—writing stories and books—is crucial
to me. I look for things to entertain me outside myself; and that's no good. When I write, and don't
feel self-disgusted and depressed, it becomes possible
to entertain myself. If I can't do that it's a living
death. I don't want to forget this. Therefore, I need
a tape recorder."

"No, Jesse, I don't do well with a tape recorder."

"Why?"

"I don't know."

"Because it seems voyeuristic and pornographic to
hear sex talk played back at you? Because of your
legal position?"

"Neither."

"Then what? Are there other possibilities?"

"Maybe."

"Like what?"

"I don't know."

"Then I'll want to rely on your memory to recall things to me. Because if I forget the next day. And they are vitally important revelations. Will they have the same significance next day? It's life and death. I must remember. . . ."

"Do you trust my memory?"

"Is your memory that good?"

"Pretty good."

She demonstrates.

"Yes. That's good. But if you fail with your memory or I'm not satisfied with its retrievability powers, then I want the machine. And if you won't give me the machine, then I'll get someone else with a machine."

"I'm replaceable," she says.

"I guess I mean that."

"I think you do. Better to replace me with a person than with a machine."

"I just mean a machine is sure. I could get it all back."

"It's impersonal though. A machine is inanimate."

"But—"

"I've had enough of this subject."

"But look, I could play it the next day, study it, write it down and take notes."

"Sure," she says, "and if you find that it doesn't
have the same significance then you'll say it's because you smoked when doing it and then would
smoke to listen to the tapes, and then you'd spend
four or five hours a day stoned and listening to tapes,
and then at night too, and then you're dependent on
it totally and don't use your own straight head. That
would hurt me."

"Yes, I can see that."

"That would really hurt me."

In bed, she tries to explain again how she feels
about the tape recorder. I have my own private rea-
sons for not wanting to use the machine. I don't feel
good about it. You'd be doing a monologue. I would
have nothing to do with it. I don't like tape re-
corders. It's just a feeling I have. I don't know.
That's my thing. It doesn't all go back to you, Jesse.
You're not the center of it all. I have my own feelings about not wanting to use a tape recorder. You
were the center of your mommy's universe, you told
me, and of Paula's, and everything had to meet your
needs. But understand this, I *don't* . . . want . . .
the . . . tape . . . recorder. My feelings. Michele's
feelings.

December 16.

Zonked out reading the Bible. Look what it says
in Leviticus 26: "And ye shall eat the flesh of your

182 TWO-WAY TRAFFIC

sons, and the flesh of your daughters shall ye eat."
Nice God, really nice God.

"You use that thing down there really well," I
say.
"Thank you," she says.
"I find you very smart, but also I find you a good
fuck, really good."
"A girl likes to hear that. It's good to know, and
to do it with someone who likes the same things."
We're eating fruit salad to cool off our hot and dry
mouths whereupon she fishes out my limp cock and
puts a cherry on the head. We sit and watch it un-
coil, rise up under our gaze. It was giggly. It was
cute. It was okay. "It reminds me of a dirty joke
from junior high school," I say. "But it's not *dirty*.
You don't feel that way, do you?" No, no, no, no.
"Do you take as long to come with other girls?"
I am aware of the complications, my history, and
a variety of different answers present themselves, a
discourse maybe, until I decide on the truth.
"No. . . ."

It is as though every day when I learn something
new I must fit it into the puzzle. How does it fit?
Does it validate? Or invalidate?
Waiting for kinky-haired, strangely-shaped Sally,

with whom I have made love in the grand old erotic
tradition and who this evening I will fuck well and
who will fuck me back well and true. Ernest and
Hemingway.

Two nights now I haven't seen Michele.

With Sally, her husband is in shock. They just
separated a couple of weeks ago.

She smokes a lot—socially, she says.

"He stood in the doorway of our apartment,"
Sally said. "He had come up for some clothes. It was
in the evening, about eight thirty. The kids were in
their room. I mean, it was *his* house, until a couple
of weeks ago. He stood there like a stranger in the
doorway, without knowing what to say, in the hallway, while I went to get him his underwear. I felt so
bad for him."

I know the feeling, I told her. It's like being insane, or feeling that the world has gone off balance.

Met a taxi driver the other day who said, "Everyone from the president on down should drive a taxi
for a few months. You see what's really going on with
people. I raised four girls on my experience driving
a taxi. I learned that people got to talk to other people. I always talked to my daughters and encouraged
them to talk to me. And I learned about unity and
the lack of unity among people. That's what causes

all the prejudice. And money causes disunity. And greed. And mostly it's all about fear. Projecting fear makes the other guy afraid. You got to stop projecting so much fear. But first you got to not feel fear and that's a difficult thing for most people."

Said another driver: "I could have arrested a thousand people over the last eight years, the things I've heard here. Smoking marijuana in the back. I tell them to stop or I'll stop at the next police station. Peddlers cutting stuff up in the back. I had only one case of people fucking in the back. A Chinese guy. He was the only one. Lots of finger fucking back there, but only one instance of actual fucking."

So Monday I went down to the Motor Vehicle Bureau to get my chauffeur's license. Easy enough. Six bucks and they transfer your operator's license.

Tuesday I went to the Universal Company and filled out some forms that Max gave me there. On 46th Street, a block from the Hudson River, in a factory district. Max said the day shift starts between six thirty and seven. Get up at six o'clock? I must really be crazy. For three months now I've been getting up at ten, eleven, noon. "Tomorrow," said Max, "go to the Metropolitan Taxi Board of Trade. They'll give you a medical, a psychological test, a geography test. They'll ask you like, 'Where's Penn Station, where's the Hilton Hotel.' Simple stuff like that."

I haven't told Tommy I love him in a long time. I haven't in a long time told him that something he did made me proud of him.

"That's a proudful thing," he once said of an accomplishment of his.

"What does frustrated mean?" he asked me another time.

A dream of going up the stairs to Hebrew School. (The dream was December 19.) With my dog. Hearing Mrs. Yehoshofat's voice as though I'd heard it yesterday. Very vigorous, booming, enthusiastic. "Is somebody there?" she called out. She came out for a look and I ducked down the stairs, didn't want her to see me, didn't want to make any explanations to her. Sitting at the bottom of the stairs was a girl, a hippie in a cape, with a dog.

The central paranoia: I read it in a magazine article. What is my central paranoia? Fear. Some fear of something, loneliness, lack of love, loss of love. Her circus fantasies in the spring, being fucked by white horses and acrobats diving from 100 foot platforms into her. Her Dylan records. "My father

watched me all the time, and now you're doing it,"
she said. Her traffic tickets.

Phone conversation with my mother:
"My mother was a designer of women's clothes.
My father was a tailor. He worked for an outfit."
"So how come you never told me that before.
What was the mystery?"
"You never asked me."
"Your life is a secret."
"It's no secret. I stayed home for many years taking care of my mother. My brother Sol told my
father he should let me go to business, that it wasn't
good for me. Let her go to work he'd say."
"Nh? . . ."
"Dad got his job with Palmer's the day your
brother was born. He felt Ben brought him good
luck. That's how he felt. . . . I had a lot of nice
guys after me. I don't know why I married him. I've
often asked myself why I married him. . . . You
two boys were my whole life. I was happy with the
two of you at home. . . . No two boys ever had more
love than you two. . . . We took you to restaurants
and museums. We sent you to camps. . . . I was
tempted to leave him time and time again. He made
me sick, that man. I was never like this. . . . Kids
these days can leave their spouses but I thought,
'What could I do with two children?' . . . He

doesn't make any sense sometimes. I'd ask his sisters, 'Was he always like this?' I'd ask them over and over. He picked up right where his own father left off."

Janet says: "You will never have a relationship with them because it is continuously hypocritical and irrational. They can do nothing for you except make you more angry at them."

Says S.: "Your hands are fantastic. You're really unbelievable. You said you didn't know how to play a musical instrument, but that's not true. You know how to play the pussy."

"Probably."

"And the way you—you were in me for the entire record, thirty minutes of *The Cream*. That "Train Time" part, ahhh. I've never felt anything like that. God, that was a whole new experience. . . . I lost track how many times I came. I fainted once."

"I'm impressed with myself even. Sometimes I feel like I'm never going to come. But I always do, finally."

"Like cannon salvos. It feels like you come in cannon salvos."

"I had a three- or four-month rest. Maybe that's why."

"Does it work that way?"

"It never happened to me before. It was the longest sexual freeze since the onset of . . . adolescence."

"You fuckhead, you're too fucking much."

M. says: "Screwing isn't the same as making love. Maybe screwing is all you're capable of these days."

A publisher has accepted my new book, the one I wrote last year. *Waiting*. The editor there said he thought it was a major work.

S. is philosophical, apparently, from what she says, more so than her husband from whom she just separated. She ranges from hip talk to radical politics to the fruits of three years' analysis: "You have to know your emotions to be able to express them." She has a joie de vivre. She has hair like steel wool worn Afro style. A fixed nose. I went to a Yoga class with her at Swami Satchidananda's.

"I forgot to tell you about something that happened to me in May or June. I bought two pair of good pants, expensive bell-bottoms. And after a week or two I had to take them to a tailor and I asked them to take the bell-bottoms out. A Puerto Rican tailor around the corner from where I lived. I was in a sweat. It was a hot day. Around the same time I stopped smoking grass, stopped listening to music, stopped seeing women."

You fell back on an earlier image, your father's
image of you. You disliked yourself enormously. Too
bad you're not writing these days. What a great moment in literature that would be, going to a tailor
to have the bells taken out of your pants. . . . Did
they buy all your clothes for you?

"Yes."

Resolution: "Take the elevator instead of walking
up the stairs to the second floor. That way I'll meet
more people in my building."

December 27.
My father keeps calling me. One day to announce
that my brother has changed his plans and is not
coming in from Switzerland after all. Come to dinner, any of the next three nights. I said no for each
night. Two days later he called, wondering if I was
free that afternoon, to "shmooze." Sorry. And again
two days later, to tell me they still had lots of food in
the house, stocked up for Ben's visit. Any night
would be okay. Sorry. Well when are we going to see
you? Next week. I'll call you. The question is: why
can't I just tell him to leave me alone, not to call,
that it is pointless, crazy, that he is poison to me.
Probably he wouldn't believe me. Would I believe it
if Tommy came up to me one day and said, "Dad,

let's break it off because it's hypocritical, dishonest and poisonous." Probably not.

Janet: They developed hiding their feelings to a fine art. . . . Through fear and intimidation they raised you.

Take it easy. Don't overdo it. Careful.

Her mottoes.

Since she had no other life, and I was her whole life, the reason she so much worried about me and wanted me all the time to be careful was because my death would bring about her death. "You two boys were my whole life." She told me that on the phone just the other day. If I was her whole life, taking me away means she has no other life.

She cleaned me and the house like she cleaned herself. She cautioned me against taking any chances and doing anything extravagant like she cautioned herself. Be clean and be careful.

You are mine. You are not you and yours; you are mine.

Before you do anything, look around cautiously, exercise extreme care, look to the right and left and over your shoulder. Be extremely hesitant. And then take a careful step.

Michele wanted to have a long talk on Sunday. We did. She wanted to know where things stood.

Was I seeing someone else? Was I involved? Why was I doing this? (That day I awoke at Sally's apartment, hung around till about two and did some errands with her. I got back to my place, took a shower, and at four Michele came.

I have one smoke before she arrives, and, seeing her, I know I haven't been able to make the mental switch. She sits on the bed that I don't sleep on. I look at her like a stranger of sorts. Small talk, accusations, discomfort, for a half hour. We have a smoke. We go into the other room. I get really stoned. I am nodding. "I don't know where you're at today, Jesse, but you're not here with me. You're off someplace." We sit facing each other. Then I stare down at the radiator. I say things like, "Without mercy, men are like beasts. . . . Be sympathetic to others. . . . Everyone is entitled to happiness." She says, "I've been rubbing myself against you and trying to get you to see me, much less trying to get you to make love to me, and you've been ignoring me. You're not in the same room with me."

I winced under her rebukes. Michele, I'm sorry.

She asked me what Sally is like, and I asked her to guess. She did, partly right. "More like Paula than me, right?"

We go on as I come down a little about why I am doing this complex thing. Is it because I don't like Michele? No, I like Michele. Is it security in num-

bers? as she suggests. Not wanting to get involved?
To see who else is out there? To make up for the
period of isolation? Yes, all that. A reaction against
monogamy? Yes. To prevent possessiveness? Because I have been so long without love that I want
a girl loving me daily?

Michele says: "Maybe screwing is all you're capable of these days. But it's not the same as making
love."

I tell her I am making decisions solely on the basis
of having fun.

The focus of your attention is solely on your social
life, she says. It's true. Why not? What else do I
have to do with my time?

We part, sadly.

I am not as suicidal as I was a scant three weeks
ago. I had sat there and told Janet it was all I had
been thinking about for the past sixteen hours. I
don't know how it finally got stopped. Why? Maybe
it has to do with shrugging my shoulders and saying
"fuckit" and seeing what happens, with Sally, Michele, Paula, the kids, the world. Recently, with all
my fucking one girl one night and another the next
—one of the side effects is that I don't think suicidal
any more. Therapy? But alternate fucking is confusing. Do I do it for fun? To sneer at women? To
prove my masculinity? I ought to try beautiful
women, really beautiful women, so long as I'm at it.

Sally has remarked on how filthy my bathroom is. Her husband wouldn't live like that, alone. He is apparently more self-sufficient than I (who isn't?). "He can cook and buy all kinds of things for himself."

This Jamaican grass is excellent.

Sally is a kind of hip Jewish social butterfly of the upper West Side. She has a raspy voice, Jewish hair, Jewish face, and much gusto and entertainment. A fertile, understanding, humorous head. Sort of a healthy head, I think.

I keep making a mistake thinking there are two women in my life, Sally and Michele. There are three: Paula. No, four, if you include Janet. And five if you include my mother.

Molly dug a hole in the bedspread. Probably because of her hysterical pregnancy. I find her sleeping in the bathtub, to cool off her swollen, hot breasts. Sally's screwy-nice friend Dolores says she milked her poodle for three months, having started it to alleviate the dog's false pregnancy. Imagine anyone milking his (in this case *her*) dog for three months. "It used to get me all hot doing it," Dolores added.

Michele is sick with the flu and a stomach thing. She calls and wants to know if I can come down to keep her company. I can't because I have a date with Sally to go to a concert at the Felt Forum: *The Band.* Michele wants me to make up mind about the weekend, whether or not I'm going. I said I'd try to see into my mind. She says she doesn't know what my mind is doing, where my head is at. I tell her that makes two of us, S. having just left after spending the night here, and Paula coming in a half hour with the kids. Sunday.

Paula was two hours late with the kids. She still had her laryngitis. I had gotten Tommy a transistor radio with a colorful band, and a battery-operated train set. He went right at it, loving the way it clickity-clacked around and around the tracks. I got Suzie a pull dog. Paula sat for a while, smoking a hash pipe ("I didn't buy it—I traded something for it.") She gave me a copy of the newest Panther paper, which she says she helped make possible by cooking for a Panther commune in the East Village. She told me about her new boyfriend, Peter, and how he is sick in his lymph glands. "He used to be a teacher until two years ago but he quit and he's done nothing but fuck four or five times a day since then. He's so beautiful. He loves to fuck. He just knows how to touch a girl and she goes all squishy for him. But he's sick now and I told him I'd cook for him when he's better." I showed her my taxi license with the picture. She examined it, stayed another five minutes, in which she made two phone calls, and then left.

I took the kids over to the Piersons, up in the old neighborhood in Riverside Park where the hills are steep. We went sledding on friends' sleds. Tommy and I went down on the round spinner, spinning round and round with him screaming, laughing. He made a couple of trips on the other sled, with runners, and pretended he knew how to steer, narrowly missing trees and benches. I held Suzie most of the time, handing her off to Eddie or Gail when I went down with Tom. He made dozens of rides, solo, with Bobby, Ed's kid, with Ed, with assorted daddies and little boys and girls. He took a spill and hurt his arm and didn't want to sled any more so we went to Ed's house where I flirted with his wife and a friend of theirs, Judy, recently separated, who seemed to have heard too many stories about me from them. Suzie had a shit and I had no extra pampers with me so we scoured the building and finally found some.

At five I took them and the dog back to my place, nearly freezing waiting for a taxi. We collected the radio, the hats, gloves, book and Paula's check and took a taxi down to the Chelsea, where Paula said she'd be cooking dinner for Nissim. At the elevator a Latin-looking girl floating past playing the har-

monica, eying me and smiling. Tommy led me to
Nissim's room where he apparently had been many
times. Nissim and two philosopher-friends talked
cosmology and evolution and how the Chinese were
right to invade the corrupt Tibetans, and how as a
result Tibetan spirituality was released all over the
world as lamas fled in all directions, to New Jersey,
Florida and Virginia City, Nevada, the latter, America's new spiritual capital, according to Nissim. A
lot of talk about Yoga and knowledge of previous ex-
istences. Tommy asked Paula if I could stay for dinner, and I did, about a half hour. I saw a camel
saddle I bargained for in a market in Old Jerusalem
—Nissim sitting on it. Paula had decided unilaterally
it was hers.

"Why isn't Tommy going to a kindergarten?" I
ask Paula.

She changes the subject. Tommy looks fearful and
bored in the hot, candlelit little room. "Daddy, can
you take me to the beach next summer?" Tommy
asks. "We'll see."

They all suddenly stood up and said they were late
for the convention. They said they were going to bust
into the American Philosophical Association convention at the Waldorf. "Are we going to the beach
this summer?" asks Tommy again. "Are we?" I tell
him the summer is a long way off. What can I say?
Yes, we'll go but only if I don't get suicidal again?

He wants a bombardier's hat—at whose suggestion
I can't imagine.

Just before we leave he whispers, "Paula lets me
smoke dope." What?

I ask her. Is it true? Do you?

Sure, she says. Just a puff. He doesn't inhale.

from notebook four

No dreams in the past two weeks. Am I repressing something? Or in living more do I pay less attention to night and sleep?

A strange, businesslike letter from my mother arrived today.

> Dear Jesse,
> We thought you might give us the courtesy of a call. Since you haven't done so I am taking the initiative of writing this message to you. We are still interested in your welfare as always, and hope you are keeping well and taking care of yourself.
> I hope you have changed your unhealthy opinion of us, as your parents, our conscience is clear. We feel that we have done as much as we possibly could for you over the years and more—If you

think back carefully we were always ready to help
you at every beck and call.

You messed things up yourself including your marriage, and you are trying to blame us for everything. Why not blame yourself and Paula? Why
are you keeping the children from seeing us? Do
you want them to forget us?

You have taken a dislike to everyone in our family.
Why? Don't think you can truly answer this at all.
My family has wished you well at all times and
constantly keep asking about you—We do hope you
are now in a better state of mind, and when you
feel up to it give us a buzz.

In spite of everything you have said and done, we
still love you and always have and will.

As always,
Mother

Today, with Sally, I went to Riverside Church to
read names of the Vietnam war dead at a continuous
name-reading marathon. I wanted to pronounce
them right. "Jesse Roy Leighton, Oakville, Mis-
souri, dead in Vietnam." Wait twelve seconds till
the light flashes. "Danny Biggs, New Hope, Indiana,
dead in Vietnam."

When I told Janet the story about Tommy and
Paula letting him take a toke (I don't know if it's
true or not), she said, well, don't make it sound for-
bidden to him, because that will only make it seem

attractive, but don't let him think it's a cure-all or a
very big deal, on the other hand.

Last night, Monday, I broke a date with Sally
to spend some time with Arnie. (Subtly, Janet goes
on encouraging me about "male companionship.")
Arnie brought his friend Gregg over, a former editor
turned taxi driver who picks up fares on the basis of
whether he likes their looks or not and whether he
thinks he'll enjoy talking with them. He goes to parties that his fares invite him to, parks the cab and
leaves it sitting there for hours while he's inside. His
girlfriend was from California, a waitress in New
York organizing a theater troupe in California. We
ate at Max's and discussed New Year's parties. At
the restaurant Arnie and I spotted a Polish waitress
who, when we heard her speaking, we immediately
knew had spent time in Israel, in Tel Aviv. We were
right on all accounts. She was surprised. The only
thing we didn't know was what section of Tel Aviv.
(Arnie had lived in Israel, on a kibbutz, when he was
twelve.) About Tel Aviv, we could tell by the girl's
manner and sexy haughtiness. Gregg's date said we
were teasing the girl, and that she hated men to tease
her when she was waitressing.

We smoked some joints in the car heading up to
the West End.

"Do you ever take a girl with you in the cab?" I
ask Gregg.

No, he said, because of the hot seat. It turns on
the meter as soon as someone sits down. If she came
with me, he said, she'd have to sit on the floor sort of
between the front seat and the floorboards there,
crouching kind of.

We started giggling.

But how would you introduce her to people? Say,
for example, I got in the car and saw her crouching
there. What would you say?

He shrugged, eyes twinkling.

"I'd say, 'This is my friend Carol.'"

The West End bar. Last time I was there was
with Paula, almost ten years ago, March of that
year we met and married. Ten years spent with her.
Nine years, really. It looked a little the way I remembered it inside. I remembered the booth in the
corner where I told her dirty jokes for a couple of
hours. That was unbelievable, that night. We sat
and laughed and talked. I remember calling Henry
from a phone booth there, leaving her sitting, and
asking him what he thought of my first book, which
he had just read.

I didn't faint. Or get an anxiety attack. Or
cramps. The place looked 1970-hip, not 1960s Ivy
League collegiate. So that made it seem different. I
flirted with an Australian biology teacher (Columbia) named Marianne. Told her I'd stroke her hair
when it was long next year. Complimented her in

her right places and suddenly she told me how nice she thought I was. But she was the bartender's girl. She kept pointing out Weathermen going in and out of the bathroom, and dealers going in and out of the bathroom. A girl editing an underground collegiate subscription newspaper. Marianne and I talked about the Tasmanian tiger and whether her room-mate was involved, cool, flexible, coy, challenging, and wicked.

Next day I went to the shrink's stoned. I talked a lot, maybe more than usual, the only difference; just chronology since the last time I was there. About the grass she said at least it shows a depressed person life can be enjoyed at *some* level so maybe it makes you want to try to enjoy yourself more when you're straight.

On the way back from her place I talked to a kid on the corner selling Panther newspapers.

If you've always eaten celery one way, can you learn to eat it another way? Watch and see next time. Everyone eats celery his own way—some tear off the grass at the bottom, some separate the pieces into individual stalks. Eating celery is as individual a matter as eating fried eggs sunny-side up.

Yesterday Sally said my marriage was a re-creation of my womb, of my childhood. "Excuse me for say-

ing it, for being so blunt, but it's kinda obvious."
The nerva the cunt saying a thing like that.

Smashed. New Year's Eve. Seven P.M. December
31, 1969. The end of the decade of the sixties. Look
what I did in the sixties. Paula, Tommy, Suzie, novels published and unpublished, hundreds of articles
and short stories, traveling in Israel, Turkey, India,
Norway, two dogs, hundreds of baby-sitters, two
walk-up addresses and two elevator addresses, an
overweight, overtalkative, bubbly, flat-chested,
cheery redheaded wife, a movie made from a book,
friends like Tony, Bud, Norman. Something swells
in me, like grief, or panic, some shocking it's-too-late
realization. Was I unconscious all those years? Or
unconscious now. Living in a kibbutz with Paula,
the trip to the Himalayas, the honeymoon article research, the summers at the sea. How different will
the 1970s be? Ten more revolutions of the earth. A
voice on the radio says how about leaving the failures
in the sixties and taking the lessons and successes
into the seventies. A new decade. My marriage coin-
cided with the decade of the sixties. Married in
June, 1960, in a rabbi's backyard. A voice on the
radio says innocence is the first thing a man loses,
hope is the last. I'm scared.

"Mrs. Robinson" is playing, a record Paula and I
used to fuck to in the summer of 1968. I feel old.

Shit, why did I fuck up my wrist, my finger, my
beard? I could solve it though. Because I don't like
feeling like some now-Italo Svevo. It's like I'm following myself around making notes on me. Why am
I compelled to keep writing this thing?

On this last day of the 1960s I am really stoned.
If there is a 1980 for me I wonder what my children
will be then, and where. And me. With another
wife? More children? Alone? Unlikely. Like writing
to a time capsule. *Doctors say there is no reason for
the human body to die.* The voice on the FM. I am a
much better writer now than I was at the end of the
fifties. I understand people more now than at the
end of the fifties. I am a better lover now than then.
I understand something of what's the matter with
me now and didn't then. I am a much better dancer
now. So I'm ahead. Mommy and Daddy, leave me
alone. No more appeasement either, mother appeasement or father appeasement. Our meetings
are a series of Munichs. I'm thirty-three. Why do
they treat me like I'm three? Ruben loved doing
that business at the hospital with the bank and the
money, and my mother with bringing me clean
laundry and picking up dirty laundry, baby can't
clean his clothes, Mommy do it for you. And bringing me fruit. Fruit! Fruit to her baby in the loony
bin, finally where their craziness finally brought me.
Fuck them. Why do I even have to say this? I'm too
old. I should be past that stage.

Who was I with New Year's Eve, December 31, 1959? Probably Lisa. But where? That's the sort of thing Sam should remember. He's good at that. It could be important to know. That Christmas I walked around reciting the "Twelve Days of Christmas" song over and over and over in my mind—to keep myself from thinking, panicking, feeling. But that too passed. I don't remember how.

Dinner at Sally's, with Arnie and Sally's friend Jill. Met one of Sally's baby-sitters, a robust, big-chested, perfectly complexioned girl—serene, peaceful eyes and a little half smile. Just gorgeous. Arnie thought she was his date. No such luck.

We had decided to try to make four or five parties tonight—where we didn't know anybody, and drift in and out of different worlds.

The first was on 60th Street, between Lexington and Third. A friend of Arnie's would be there, someone he went to public school and camp with. A drinking party? Drug party? Orgy? Beautiful people? A bummer? It was a floor through, with balloons on the wall, party noisemakers, a bar, and a bunch of wisecracking kids, two of whom knew Arnie. ("He's kind of into money," was all Arnie said about him before we got there.)

They wore Ivy League clothes, had short haircuts, and made a lot of talk about making it big in the

new year. A big pile. "Hal baby, this is gonna be our
year, right?" People with baggy old suits, a lot of
young Charley salesmen types, two cops in training.
Their girls were imported from the Bronx and
Queens, in Korvettes dresses. Somehow they'd lost
step with their generation. 1950-ish-looking people.
Sally and Jill corner a kid (the cop in training?)
and tell him not to go into the bathroom because
two people were in there fucking. From the look on
the guy's face you could see he never before heard a
girl say "fucking." They added details. I played
along. We said we wanted to see how they reacted to
people when they came out. "Actually, there are two
girls and a guy in there," Sally said. The cop-in-
training didn't know what to say. Except that he
hung around the bathroom door till the door opened
and a guy came out and Sally screamed, "What happened to the other two?" The guy checked his fly
and said, "What?" Then Jill asked him about the
bathroom's decor, the flush of the toilet, the water
pressure ("Was it a strong or a listless flush?"), and
did he remember by chance the color of the shower
curtain?

It wasn't much fun, so we left. The next one was
Sally's friend's party at "a prominent lady journal-
ist's," also on the East Side. Kay Zentorr. I'd read
her articles for years, met her once, briefly, talked
to her on the phone once. She got her start writing
an exposé about Playboy bunnies when she was a

bunny for a month in New York. Very hip-chic rich
apartment. Glass-framed posters, lots of steel and
glass, furry rugs, an entirely ego-centered, fashion-
able, contemporary ambience. It looked a little "I
made it folks." The place was packed and well-ca-
tered. Successful-looking older types. More busi-
nessy people than artsy people. Respectable politics
people. "Kay," I asked her, "who are all these people? What brings them together here?" She looked at
me oddly. "They're my friends," she said. They
looked a little on the plastic side, but then who am I
to say. They looked more like someone's acquaintances than friends. Sally's buddy Fran was there and
seemed to go all drippy for Arnie. "I could fall in
love with him," she whispered to Sally.

Party number three was at the home of a philoso-
phy teacher from Columbia. We thought that
sounded more interesting. A West Side address—
102nd Street. He turned out to be a Russian history
teacher at LIU. A lonely middle-aged man with
long beard and peeling ceilings. He had put up
streamers and balloons. He gave us wine. The six
people there were students, somewhat similar-looking
to the first party people. Button-down shirts and
short haircuts and girls in prim dresses who sat quietly and primly waiting to be spoken to. We stayed
twenty minutes or so, and started getting profoundly
depressed. Into the car. Smoked two big joints. The
choice was between 74 Greene Street where some

Indian students were giving a party and Sam's place. Greene Street was a long drive; Sam and Hilda lived a few blocks from the teacher's place. We chose Sam and Hilda's house, even though Sally whispered that she wanted to go home and fuck.

One thirty. Sam's house. Sally still wanted to go home and fuck. She was tired from making all those different worlds. Sam found Joan who said she remembered being with me outside someone's brownstone and looking at a nameplate. On December 31, 1959. We talked about my summer journey for the first time since it happened. I had spent almost every night for two weeks with them to no avail, seeking company, talk, fighting loneliness. Hilda said she was angry at Bud for not coming down from Montreal. "He was the only one who could reach you then." When we had dinner at that Chinese restaurant that time in July, the four of us, Bud had said, "Watch him, he's ready to go." I went. Hilda said she talked to him on the phone for a half hour begging him to come down to talk to me. He said he was setting up a show and he got married all of a sudden. "I said, 'Okay, but you could talk to him.' Nobody else could get into your head." I wish Sam could, I said, but I just never had that kind of thing with him. Hilda angry at me for choosing a woman shrink over a man. I explained why. I told her I knew what she was thinking. The more I talked the more convincing, and after a while she said, "Must be a pretty good shrink. Stick with her. You seem okay."

Sally shooting me angry glances for getting so wrapped up with Hilda. (Later she spat, "You really like her. No wonder your friend gets uptight when the two of you are together.") Others leave. I turn up the stereo. Sam turns it down. Sam baby, what've you been doing the last ten years since bachelordom? Unemployed actor in perpetuity. Fucking, he said. Lots of fucking. What did you think I was doing? Isn't that all *you* do these days? Sam, where was I when I got married? Who was I? What did you think of Paula? Here comes the marathon, the sensitivity thing. Hilda, who was I when you first met me? What did you think Paula's thing was all about in the spring? Arnie, when we played tennis what did you think of me? Sally? They all did it, but Sally didn't want to. She wanted to go home and fuck. I was stoned on grass and flying on champagne. I could ask anybody anything.

Sam: "Paula never listened. She only talked. I thought she was very neurotic. A bore."

Hilda: "I thought you had a happy marriage the first time we met."

Sam: "I thought you and Paula were kind of having fun with the grass, kind of cute. I guess I don't really know what happened to you and her."

Hilda: "I do. A little. It's not black and white, not all you wronged. Paula couldn't sit by forever

while you did your clickety-clack thing on the typewriter."

Arnie: "Paula's being experimental and trying out
a style. . . . When we played tennis you didn't put
shots away. You hesitated and volleyed when you
should have put them away."

Sally didn't want to do this business and Sam got
angry at her. Hilda confided to me she thought Sally
was hard and tough, aggressive and unfeminine.
Sally confided to me she didn't like Sam, that he
didn't know or understand what had happened to
Paula and me and that it frightened him, and that
he didn't know himself either. Hilda and Sam liked
Arnie though. At a quarter to four we left. Tried to
fuck at Sally's place but too drunk. A shower. Tried
again. Couldn't come so drunk. Sally tried cherries
on my cock, peanut butter after that. Nothing doing. Hello 1970.

A New Year's Day party. First some friends of
Sally stopped by her place (more of her friends who
she says see me as an instant replacement for her
husband Marty) and we smoked some parsley-TCH
joints and got absolutely numb. The party was on
Riverside Drive, in the apartment of a husband-
and-wife lawyer couple. They had a big teen-age
Swiss au pair, beaded and belled, taking care of their
kids. At least a hundred people there. A lovely tall

girl in a décolletage green velvet dress, working for
the National Commission on Crime and Delin-
quency, and why didn't I get her name? Tables of
food and hors d'oeuvres. The husband of the apartment tells me he and his wife specialize in getting
political prisoners out of solitary confinement
—lately. Also there was a social-climby editor I
knew and a psychiatrist-friend of Sally's who
wouldn't talk to Sally's friend Jill, also there, because she was his patient last year. I tried to tell
him that was being unreasonable. So many people.
Two girls who kept asking me for dope. "We looked
around the room and decided that you would probably have some, and that one there, and him, but
we've already asked them and they said no." One of
the girls had sliced her pinky and was wearing a
bandage. "Did you ever hear of someone trying to
commit suicide by slicing their pinky?" she asked.
Sally insisted I leave with her because these people
were all friends of hers and Marty's and Marty was
expected any moment, and she felt that would have
been awkward. I really didn't want to leave. I really
like all Sally's parties. How does someone have so
many friends? Do you have to work at it?

Back at her place it gets bad. She attacks my politics as fascistic. "I'm letting some kind of a fascist
in my bed," she says snidely. Then we argue over
her not wanting me to stay over because she and
Marty and their two shrinks—four people in all—

think it would be unhealthy for the kids so soon.
They need more time to get used to Daddy's not being around. But I don't like getting dressed at two
o'clock in the morning and going out in the cold.
It feels awful. It makes me feel used and studdish
and stupid. "You could be more considerate of my
children's welfare," she says. "I've raised them pro-
tectively and I'm being consistent," she adds. "You
won't compromise."

I split. I put on my coat and just split.

Next weekend Paula comes by with Tommy and
Suzie, the latter coughing, the former beaming and
smiling and healthy. Paula: "Can I borrow the Chinese fur hat? The car window's stuck and the heater
doesn't work. It's really cold in the car." "Sure," I
say.

Suzie is talking more. "Funny. . . . Mollio. . . .
Am thirsty, Jesse." She's also pouting and sulking
more too.

We go over to Sally's. First buying some food and
some Neo-Synephrine for Suzie's cold. The food bag
breaks on Broadway, the bottom gives out, and a
bottle of apple juice crashes on the sidewalk. People
pass by, wondering what I'm going to do about it. A
girl offers to hold Suzie. Tommy says, "Shit, can we
go back and get some more at the store?"

Sally looks so surprised, watching me play with

the kids. She'd never met them before. "You're a
whole other person this way. You have a whole other
life." Tommy plays with her son John, wrestling,
building with blocks, riding his bike (he'd like a
bike), listening to Beatles records, eating. Charley,
three, keeps taking a toy chair and a plastic cord
away from Suzie and she cries and Tommy calls
Charley a shmuck. I tell Tommy a story about an
alligator who a snake calls a crocodile and then gets
called a big worm. In the end they patch it up.
Tommy tells me a story about a squirrel, a tiger, and
a bunch of bananas. Sarah tells a story about talking
elevators.

Tommy: "Where's your father?"

John: "He doesn't live with us any more."

Tommy: "How come?"

John: "My mother and my father don't get along."

Tommy: "Mine too. They'd argue all the time."

Marty comes, Sally's husband. He picks up the
kids. We make small talk, sitting in the living room,
his living room, for which he pays the rent. I know
his feeling, to see someone else in your environment
with your wife. I feel bad. He doesn't stay long. After he leaves Sally tells me he told her he sees me as
an instant replacement. Suzie naps. I walk the dog.
Sally offers Tommy ginger ale. "I'm not sure I can
have it. I'm not sure if it's because I'm a macrobiotic
or a Sagittarius."

Paula comes, after demonstrating at the Museum

of Modern Art. She is impressed with Sally's big
apartment, reminiscent of ours on Riverside Drive.
She tells Sally: "Don't give it up. Don't give up your
comforts. Don't move to the East Village. Keep your
heat and your washing machine." She seems impressed by Sally's politics. The two of them swap
grass.

They seem to get on like real buddies. They establish they are both Sagittarius.

"Where are your kids?" asks Paula.

"My husband picked them up. He took them overnight."

Paula laughs. "Far out. When'd you split?"

We could come over sometime, Paula says, thinking aloud, and your husband, too, and we could all
rap, the four of us, and maybe get some things
straight. Your husband could bring a friend, and
then. . . . No, she says, catching herself in the fantasy, maybe I don't really want to do that. Maybe it
wouldn't be such a good idea.

Before he leaves Tommy gives me his Krishna
beads.

Paula drives us down to a Japanese restaurant on
37th Street, on her way down. She never stops talking, about Nissim's heroin addiction, her acid trips,
New Year's Eve at the Elgin Theatre.

When we get to the restaurant, and leave the car,
Sally says, "I like her, Christ, I really like her. I
mean she's *m'shuga,* but she's very likable. Thing is

she never listens to anyone. She only talks. She doesn't
hear."

(Janet: "Sally is intimidating and dominating."
Me: "I know.")

Telling Sally my theories on living in the city, the
killing of the spirit here, the country, the communes,
politics, living alone. She concedes I may be as
smart as her. We discuss sharing, group living, divi-
sion of property, tribal warmth. We drink a bottle
of Piper champagne.
"You won't be able to drink Piper on a commune,"
Sally comments.

Drove my taxi today. Turned off the alarm clock
at 5:30 A.M. Got to the garage an hour later. Drove
out in blackness and couldn't figure out how to turn
off the off-duty sign. Stopped another taxi who
showed me how. First fare was a Puerto Rican and a
girl. Six blocks: thirty-five cent tip. Then to the
West Side Airlines Terminal, then to the East Side
Airlines Terminal. A girl going from Lexington
Avenue in the Sixties to Park Avenue in the Eighties.
"My mother wants to borrow my vacuum cleaner.
She's got a ten-room apartment and two in help and

she needs *my* vacuum cleaner." "To the Chase Manhattan Plaza," said a Waspy type. Couldn't get out
of the Wall Street area. Lost for half hour or so.
Picked up two freaks on Church Street heading for
East 9th. One of them had been in Vietnam. "There's
a big difference even between the guys from Kentucky, the ones from the city and the ones from the
sticks. Those Kentucky hillbillies were the most
bloodthirsty GIs over there." A guy going to the
State Supreme Court Building. "Step on it. I gotta
compensation case." He gave me a dollar-fifteen tip
on an eighty-five cent ride. Down at Grand Street
and Henry Street, a whole other world. What are all
these old Jews still doing here? "I send my son to
the Downtown Community School," said my fare.

I stop on 6th Street to see Tommy and Suzie.
Paula is surprised. "Daddy, Paula thinks I should
live with you a while." Paula asks me about my I
Ching. I tell her a friend of Sally's did it for me the
other night. Number 11. Peace. "No kidding!"
That's what Nissim rolled, she said. Tommy: "Did
you hear me?" A girl named Volevie sleeps in their
other room. Paula still has the Chinese fur hat she
borrowed from me. Her car was stuck on ice. I tried
pushing it off with the taxi. Didn't work. Tommy
sat down on the front seat with me, turning on the
fare—the hot seat wires. Lots of kisses for Tom. I
drive them to a gas station that has a tow truck.
"That's groovy that you're driving a taxi," she says,

getting out. Uptown I find a model on Sixth Avenue: "I have to pick up my wig. . . . I am from Czechoslovakia." Four dollar fare. . . . "It's on the right side of the street, young man," said the old lady accompanied by a Jamaican nurse. The car keeps stalling when it idles. Every light, every stop, it idles. I take a guy to St. Vincent's Hospital and I take an overwrought lady to her appointment with a doctor, probably a shrink, and get her there late due to the stalling. I take the taxi back at four o'clock. Made $31.65 on the meter and nine dollars in tips. No kidney problems. The poor working man.

I get home (January 3) and T.R. calls. "I just sent you a check for $3,750. It came today." Jesus! "I just made nine dollars in tips today," I tell him. "Resign," he says. "I refused to take a lady to Jamaica," I tell him. "Are you allowed to do that?" he asks.

At Sally's she tells me she got a job with a publisher today, his private secretary, gal Friday, coffeemaker. "He's not very liberated. He's handsome, though. I'll give him a week and then I'll tell him how to stop treating me as though I was his secretary or something."

"Can I call you up at work and call you 'fuckhead'?" (Our pet-name for each other.) "Anytime," she replies.

"You have a prestige job," I tell her.

"I really feel groovy. I'm lucky. I'm white and I

have a college education. I can sell myself. But what
about a black chick. Last week a black man walked
out of Childs with an attaché case and he threw it
down and went to a construction site next door and
threw a brick through the window and got arrested.
Did his employer call him a nigger that day? That's
what I think happened."

Sally:

"I read your book. I think it's fantastic."

"Homosexuals are apolitical."

"Why we're not making it is because you think I
think you're neo-fascistic."

"I would always want to see you, whether I'm
fucking you or not."

Sally's shrink says I am selfish, ungiving and cold.

We have decided to see less of each other for a
while.

In the taxi industry I shall be known as "one-
mission Charley."

How is Casey?

I call him up. His ex-wife answers the phone. Separated wife, not yet ex-. He's gone to Mexico for
a vacation with their daughter. Why don't you stop
by?

I walk over. It's on Broadway and 78th Street. So
many girls on the street that night in maxis and
boots. Looking like girlfriends of the German Gen-

eral Staff. Peggy tells me how they're trying to work
out a fifty-fifty responsibility thing, sharing the
child, not one exclusive parent or the other. She says
their lawyers tell them the courts won't allow it. We
can just do it, she says, without courts and legal
papers.

She is painting in the studio-loft here where Casey
used to live, and the place belongs to friends of theirs
who are in Europe. Her paintings are good, and
changing a lot. But where is Casey living? I ask her.
He went back to the apartment around the corner,
and I moved out, she explained, and into here, where
I can paint. He got a housekeeper to help take care
of our daughter. Weird, man. To boot, her parents
live across the street, and she sees them in the super-
market all the time. She avoids talking to them
there, she says.

We talk about our mutual shrink, Janet, and a little gossip flows: her patients who sleep together, how
she gives you a very full hour, how she has a lot of
phone calls during sessions, how she eats lunch during sessions, her patients roaming the apartment. A
nice girl, Peggy. They were married thirteen years.

Back home, at one o'clock, I call up Sally. But her
phone seems screwed up. I have some old sleepy
grass around and I light one up and then try the
phone again.

Operator, good evening. I keep calling this num-

ber and not getting any sound at the end of my dial-
ing.

I'm sorry. I'll try it. . . . Sir? That's a busy signal.

Yes, that sounds like a definite busy signal but
when I try it I get nothing, no noise, no signal at all.

No ring *or* busy signal, sir?

That's right.

Sir, that line could be out of order.

Really?

Would you like to check it?

Yes.

One moment.

Forty rings. At least forty.

Eight-seven-three verifying.

I say: I've been trying to call 873-67 . . .

A long minute.

Busy talking, sir.

Two days later my father appears at my apartment "for a talk."

I discuss his relationship with his wife, who is my
mother, as though I am as objective as I'm pretending to be.

"You treated that woman like a slave, like a maid."

"I should have left her. She didn't obey me."

"Obey?"

"She knew I was religious. She knew what she was getting into when she married me. If she didn't like it she shouldn't have married me."

"She didn't know you'd turn into a religious fanatic."

"Is it possible you don't know that we're different with each other now?"

"Good. I'm glad to hear it. But while I was growing up you appeared to hate each other. Two weeks out of every month you weren't talking to each other. You were relaying messages to each other through me. You fought or you'd ignore each other. You showed no love for each other. The house was cold and tense all the time."

"You don't know everything. There are secrets that I'll take to my grave with me."

"I'm not interested in your secrets any more."

And.

"This routine you play with the vault key, the safety deposit box, it's been going on for ten years—you've got a new key, you tell me to give you the old key back, I get a key in the mail, a new number, on and on about your safety deposit box, every few months. It says to me, 'We're going to die soon and remember that' and that I should be a better son to you in the time remaining because if you're not it'll kill us quicker."

"That's ridiculous. That was never in my thoughts. It's simply a matter of you never know when you're going to go, and somebody should have the key to our vault just in case."

"What about your lawyer?"

"A stranger?"

"You don't trust him?"

"None of the people I talk to, my friends, do that. They all give the keys to their children, not to lawyers."

"That's a Jewish trick. It makes lots of guilt."

"I know a lot more people than you and they all do things this way."

"I'm sure they do."

"If you want to give me the keys back, then give them back."

I don't give them back.

"You think you had it so bad? You think you were the only one to have pimples? When I was a boy I had them so bad I was ashamed to go out onto the street. I would cut them with a razor and make them bleed."

And so on.

Suddenly, Karen.

I met her at a party given by one of Michele's friends, a few weeks ago. She lives in the biggest West Side apartment I've ever seen. Eight or nine rooms. She has a darkroom in back behind the kitchen. A good photographer. Her pictures on the

walls. A spotless fish tank. She is divorced three
years. Married to a crazy shrink. She went to Jamaica every summer with him. She has superfine
hair. A Canadian Wasp. Montreal-born. Father in
the diplomatic service. Her husband took her to
court seventeen different occasions over the past four
years. He stole letters from her and used them in
court as proof of adultery. Awful business with him.
He used to beat her when she yelled at him, hitting
her and whacking her around and saying he was doing it to control her hysterics. He weighed 230
pounds; she weighs 100 pounds.

We have dinner at a new restaurant on Columbus
and 92nd Street. Or is it Amsterdam and 94th
Street? I tell her how I don't want to do an ugly
courtroom scene. Margaret Mead has been to her
house for dinner. At least twice a week she goes to
Max's and has an active social life there. "A lot of
guys there won't have anything to do with me.
They're afraid of a woman with three kids." I shrug
and ask why. She looks at me funny. "You're nice,"
she says.

I made a proposition.

"How about having some of the best grass in
North America. It comes from the place where you
used to summer."

She looked at me a moment.

"Are you asking me to go to your apartment and
get stoned?"

"Yep."

She smiled. "That sounds like a good idea."

She put on her Amelia Earhart flying cap and her old long sheepskin coat. She dresses in a peculiarly grubby way.

In the taxi she asked me about my wrist scars. I tell her right out. She put a hand over my wrist and closed her eyes. Her profile is a little like the queen of England's. Kind of aristocratic Waspy-English. She says she's been trying to live down the Wasp thing her whole life.

She had the softest lips I ever kissed. She smelled lovely. She felt soft, like a child. "A thirteen-year-old is really soft, if you like 'em soft," she says. That's who I'm after, I tell her. Your daughters. She smiles. "I know how it is," she whispers. She liked the grass a lot. Wow, she kept saying. Wow. I couldn't keep my hands off her. She tried to warn me about something that would happen if she let herself go. I didn't know what she meant.

I like your head, your sense of humor, you, and the wrapping you come in. I apologize for not being able to keep my hands off you.

And then she did an incredible thing. She stood on her head. Beautiful. It changed her life, she said. Been doing it since she was twelve. Gave her a sense of the absurd, of balance. Two of her three kids can do it. Crosby, Stills and Nash singing. She talks like a kid. Kissing and playing with her delicate little

breasts. Her body hot like she is on fire inside it. She
starts up and stops. I keep smelling her, kissing her,
keep after her. She trembles and deep breathes and
stands up and walks around. She talks about trust
and knowing someone better. We talk about Yoga
and the Judeo-Christian hang-ups. You look like a
poor Russian student, she tells me. Nobody ever
called me that before, I tell her.

"Do you have a bed?" she asked. "Or do you expect me to do it on the floor with you?"

"On the floor."

Blouse. Pants. Red bikini underpants. "I've got my
period," she says, laughing. She tells me a friend
says that's the thing to say when you're in a spot
and don't want to make it with someone. My fingers
inside her hot wet middle. I take off my shirt and
she brushed her face back and forth over my chest
hairs, smelling. "So much hair. What a nice smell."
She leaves for the bathroom.

I arrange blankets on the floor. I sit Indian style
under a blanket, awaiting her return. She comes
back in and laughs when she sees me. We caress.
She takes hold of my cock and gasps. She knows
how to touch it. We go slow. She was like jelly inside. I just love the taste of her, so soft. It puts such
a good taste in my mouth, tasting and smelling her.
Her pubic down is as soft and fine as the hair on her
head. I like it too, she says, giggling. She comes
and comes and comes. Her cunt keeps spasming

around my cock. She gets terribly flushed on her neck
and shoulders.

After I got divorced everything was so different,
she said. I could never believe a man could understand me so easily, so quickly, like you. I didn't know
a man could stay inside me without coming for more
than fifteen seconds, like my husband. I was thirty-
five before I found that out, she says.

Of her parents: They should roast in hell for what
they did to me.

Will you talk to your shrink about me? she asked.

Of course. She'll be delighted with you.

I tell her I would like to take all the stuff that
Michele and Sally know about me and transfer it
into her head and we could go on from there.

Her three daughters: She won't let me sleep over.
Her husband fixed their separation agreement so
there's a clause saying no men staying over.

Karen says things like, "Well, that's what first
marriages are for. To find out things like that. How
else are you going to learn them?"

Friday night Sally and I go out to dinner with
Irene and Paul. Paul is her husband's partner, a film
editor. He is very short, messily neurotic, but mentally nimble. His big-bosomed girlfriend has recently
directed a movie. She is a self-confessed "former hippie." Has two kids, nine and twelve, whom Paul
rarely sees because he won't go to her apartment so
as not to confront the reality of her having kids—

according to Sally. At her place we make love very badly. It even hurt. She told me she loved me and I attempted to talk her out of it. Saturday morning she washed my hair. Then we went out to some art galleries—Tomi Ungerer's exhibit, and the Art Students League where her friend had some work showing. We had lunch out, took the bus uptown. "Sure you don't want to come up? Last chance?" I decline. She got off the bus without a backward glance.

Saturday night. Dinner at Karen's and meeting her three daughters. Cindy, her skinny, groovy thirteen-year-old who says her mother keeps trying to pass on her sexual hangs to her. "I'm just now coming down off a penicillin high," she tells me. A supercool, somewhat aristocratic kid. She read the book I gave her mother and said, "Mumma, he has to be kind of weird to write like that." The eleven-year-old is silent and sensitive-seeming; the nine-year-old is direct, frivolous, impish and outgoing. Easy kids to be with.

We drove in her new BMW to the movies. *Butch Cassidy and the Sundance Kid*. She did not like any of my suggestions about where to park as we cruised around. "I'm not used to that," she said. "My husband always instructed me when I drove." Same thing at dinner. She served everybody. Rather formally. I tell her that. "You tell me things about myself," she said. "I see them, too. I always wanted

someone to do that. I'm not so interested in the fact
you're a writer. It's more the delicate ability you
have to see something, to define it, and then say
something honest and direct and usually right on."
The movie was terrific.

Had a joint in the car driving back to her place.
Someone has to get up and go out in the cold and I
did it last time, she said. Another joint in her big
red bedroom. Dancing there belly to belly. When
her pants come off she gets up to go to the bathroom. You're an interrupter of passion, I tell her.
That can have its virtue, she says, smiling. It draws
out the seduction scene. She seemed skinnier to me
tonight. Her cunt is incredibly sensitive to touch. She
starts trembling right away, little moans and oh
wows. She makes it sound like she feels unbearable
tremors in her cunt. She lit a candle. We fucked and
fucked. And then talked.

"I don't like super-handsome men like Paul New-
man and Robert Redford. They're usually lousy
fucks. And besides my father is very handsome."

She tells me about her husband's $100,000-a-year
psychiatric practice in Long Island, her past boyfriend Richard, the black revolutionary (asking her
to here hold my gun while he teaches a class in
nonviolent self-defense), the children her husband
had with his new wife, a twenty-year-old kid he was
making it with. I tell her about Paula, Sally, Michele.

We make it again, this time starting from the
rear. She has the longest, most prominent clit I've
ever seen. "I think I'm going to really like making
love with you," she says. "But I won't be monoga-
mous," she says. She waves her legs delicately in the
air, like stalks in the wind, toes softly touching my
back, "the better to bring you all the way in there,"
she says. "My girls *are* terrific; anyone who can't
see that is a fool. I'm glad you like them," she says.
She gets on for an on-top ride and then I swing her
down under and then we sit up together, and on and
on, and she kept coming and coming, and I wasn't,
but she just kept coming, stupendously, using cunt
muscles to grab and squeeze. "Oh God, it just won't
stop in there." She keeps shuddering. "Oh God," she
cries. It was the longest I ever stayed inside a
woman, in my whole life. She was all fucked out.
She begged me to stop, just like in a book, that she
couldn't stand it any more.

Talked about my staying there overnight. The police will have to come to evict me, I say. "Well—"
she hesitates. Cindy's read *The Story of O,* I tell
her. ("She *has?*") Talk to Cindy about it. She'll understand. I don't want to leave. It's four o'clock.

We get two or three hours sleep. In the morning
she tells her kids to stay in the other part of the
apartment, but they've already seen my coat. We
have coffee on her bed. "You're such an easy person

to talk to," she says. "I never met anyone like you.
Your face seems to change. It always looks a little
different to me." Her eyes are loving and warm and
bright as she says this.

Eleven o'clock. Getting a bus and looking like a
dissolute ex-baron, with my turned-up collar on an
old British warmer coat and floppy long hair.

An hour later, the kids arrive with Paula. This
time Tommy looks sick. We go to the Piersons but
Tommy doesn't feel well so we come back home.
He starts running a fever, looking really droopy.
Suzie seems fine and happy. We listen to records and
read. He complains of headaches. We call the
Weather Bureau number, and my parents. My
mother gets upset about his description of his illness.
"Children don't get headaches," she says. "Did he
have a fall?"

When Paula sees Tommy she changes her mind
about participating in a four-way discussion with
Sally and Martin—which we were actually going to
do this evening. She says Tommy is feverish and
might be upset if she left him with a baby-sitter.
We'll do it another time, she says. I kiss Tommy.
He looks so awful.

Then I smoke a joint and head over to Sally's.
She and Marty are in the middle of a money discussion. She earns $116 a week and he pays her
$75 a week plus the $325 rent. We smoke and talk,

the three of us, for a couple of hours. Strangely,
I'm not the least uncomfortable. I tell Marty how
much I identify with him, with what I went through.
He winces a little when he hears. They're treating
each other so gently and sanely that I wonder where
the hostility is, why they are splitting up. I tell Marty
my feelings about environmental dislocation and
how it takes a while to get over it, that the apartment was his (as mine was mine) and how strange
it is to see someone else there (me, Nissim). "But
Jesse," Sally says, "didn't you always feel this was
my apartment?" No, I tell her, "I knew how much
it was Martin's also and I found that painful. I
found myself thinking a lot about him whenever I
was here." "You *did?*" she says. And I identified
you with Paula, in the structure of the situation,
I confess. "You *did?*" she says again.

Marty smiles. "I like you, Jesse." What can I say?
Weird. He laughs. Sally goes out. "Hey," he says,
"isn't this a great apartment? What do you say we
share it. Let's both withdraw emotional support
from her, and then I'll withdraw material support
and we'll kick her out and have a great apartment."

When she comes back in we are laughing. He's
very nice. Very kind. Sally is terribly interested in
his new girlfriend. We both tell her it's wrong. When
Marty leaves I pretend I have a virus so we don't
have to sleep together.

So we talk. Can you fuck someone's head? I ask.

Look, she says, you can come over anytime, without
calling.

   Sometimes, these days, I feel I don't give a shit.
Just to live. To see what happens. Go to Yoga
class, fuck as many women as possible, see the
movie of my book, see the shrink, make new friends,
see how different people live, get myself together
more, listen to music, smoke dope, maybe think more
about writing again. Any girl I see who is attractive
I want to fuck. It's like a compulsion. I feel it is
necessary to make plans for every night. I hardly
ever spend a night alone here any more. Sally's
friend Margaret is never alone, hasn't been alone an
hour in years, according to Sally. The same is true
of Paul, says Sally. It's not just me. A lot of people
don't like being alone. And Janet suggests I shouldn't
see my parents, that the less I see of them the
more free and independent I will be, that every
visit with them sets me back. But I haven't seen
them in six weeks, I tell her. "That's not very
long," she says. I spend money like water. One
day, in about a year, it will run out.

   Karen's husband planted dope in her dresser just
before they separated and tried to get her put in
jail. He put poison in her medicine cabinet. When

her father stayed at their apartment, because she
was afraid, he threw a wastepaper basket of cold
water over him, while he was asleep, and chased
him out of the apartment.

"What were your daughters' reactions to my staying over?"

"Well, Cindy came over twice and gave me a
hug. . . . Does she think I've been a celibate?"
(Cindy is thirteen.) "She doesn't hug me much any
more. She may have been a little patronizing with
that hug, come to think of it."

"Do they like me?"

"Yes, I've had a report. They all like you. Except
that Babette (11) has trouble relating to you. But
that's because she has trouble with men in general.
Her father. . . ."

Her skin is like powdered velvet. Recent girls' skin
in comparison, have been prickly, clammy, and rub-
bery.

At night she turned off the light when we began
to make love. "Hey," I said, "a candle at least."

"Why do you want a light?" she asked.

"I like to see you when we're making love."

"That's what I wanted to know."

She lit a candle and then I could see her. A test?

Marty calls, Sally's ex-. He offers to get me some
grass. I have a delivery coming tonight. He has

heard that Sally and I are no more together. We discuss Sally. He's very friendly. Isn't civilization wonderful?

"None of our men are able to keep Judy on their knee for very long," said eleven-year-old Babette of her nine-year-old sister. "She's so squirmy." *Our* men.

Karen seems surprised that I'm not angry at her. She called me Richard (my predecessor) while we were making love last night and had I heard it I probably would have been angry. But I didn't hear it, and didn't know about it until she told me today. I said I hadn't heard her say it and she looked suddenly confused and stupid, like she shouldn't have said anything about it. "But I didn't hardly sleep last night, it bothered me so much," she said.

She says I give off a confident aura. I find that odd. I don't *feel* self-assured.

"That night at the party where we met, you were staring at me for a long time before you started talking to me."

"I know. It worked."

She makes me feel good. Like I'm important. Like I'm special. And different. But I need a daily injection from someone, to remind me.

She says I'm too sensitive. (How many times have

people said that to me in my life? A hundred at
least.) Why can't sensitive helpless artists like you—
she says—be liberated from trivial details that drive
them wild but which others can handle easily?

Karen finds what I wanted to do with Paula, Sally
and Marty quite extraordinary. "You like to play
with fire," she says.

Karen: "Jesse, your whole trouble is you've been
fucking the wrong women."

How does she get up to get the kids off to school
after we've had three hours of sleep?

One morning, around ten o'clock, after the kids
are long gone, we poke and probe in the bathtub
under the shower. She's a regular acrobat. A try at
standing up, which never works out. Down on the
bathtub floor, eating her there, her doing me, under
the waterfall. Water, water, water. She parts my
hair to see my face. After, when my hair dries, she
runs her hands through it.

Sitting on the living-room floor, sunlight stream-
ing in through the window, eating cheese and apples
and drinking wine. "I've always wanted to have
lunch like this, but there was never the right person
to have it with," she says. We talk about going to
France, to the Caribbean, to Mexico. Brilliant sunlight in the room. Everything seems so good, so possible. I'm going to rape you, she says. I'm going to.
Okay, I say. Okay? Don't you ever want a day off?

A night off? I've got enough sleep saved up, I tell her, enough time for sleeping.

She seems irritated with my not knowing what she sees in me. I think: with all her forty-two thousand men, Why me? She says, Jesus, you're a successful writer and there are all those guys down at Max's who talk about writing novels and you just go and do them.

I have the flu, I think. Or a bad cold. Maybe I really haven't been getting enough sleep. To the virtual exclusion of everything else, I have been fucking my brains out.

Last night, at a party at Casey's, I met a girl I first saw at Peggy's show back in October, three months ago. She kept staring at me, her mouth open in wonder. "You look so different, Jesse. You looked so haggard and hungry then." Early October? I smiled. I knew what she meant. And she kept on staring, her big blue eyes trying to put two people together. She used those exact words. "It's like you're two different people. I mean I've never seen anything like it." She had a pretty face. Finally, she got up and kissed me. And she looked at me again. I felt like asking her to stop, that it was embarrassing. I told her I understood, that I was grateful to her for telling me that.

Casey was impressed with my story about the novel and the new publisher. He said why shouldn't I have written a good book? Just because I had no faith in myself in the fall. "You were pretty crazy the last time I saw you," he said.

If I don't have the flu I have something like exhaustion. I need more nights off, more sleep.

Arnie asked me how and why it was different fucking Karen and it was hard to explain.

Why should she want my money? She's not married to me any more. So why does she want my money? She's not married to me any more. So why does she want my money. She's not married to me any more.

She started in about money the other day when I brought the kids back to the museum. "I need money to do my spinning. What you're giving me isn't enough." She was interested to know how Sally supported things, who took care of the kids, how they went to school. A lot of money goes for a housekeeper, I tell her. "I thought so. I thought that about Sally," she says. Tommy looked around on the darkened street, maybe thinking about the nice time he had with Karen's daughters today, especially Judy. "If you won't give me a lump settlement (I won't) then I won't give you a Mexican divorce and you'll have to wait two years under the New York State law till we can be divorced." I shrugged: "We don't even have a legal separation yet. Why stay married

to each other legally? It's pointless. I'm not con-
nected to your life any more." She seems to know I
want to be free of her now in some official way.
"You really want a divorce now?" she asks. Why
does she seem surprised? Of course, I say; why not?
What is she getting at? I tell her she demeans herself by wanting my money, that it's parasitical and
hypocritical. She never confronts the possibility of
her making money. Her only out is the kids; she has
to be with them all the time, she thinks. I yell.
She yells. This is stupid. Hey c'mon, don't yell. I
threaten. Bad stuff. Let's do our talking with four
or two people in attendance. Pick your seconds. But
let's get it done. Okay, she says. Call your lawyer
Wednesday. Okay. By the way, Jesse, what did
they eat? What did you feed them today? Any chocolate? Any candy? Jesse: I don't feel I have to make
an accounting to you about what they eat. I kiss
the kids good-bye.

Earlier, at Karen's, Tommy and Judy got on really
well. It felt strange for him to be sitting and standing
on my shoulders in Karen's living room. It also felt
strange for Karen's kids to be on my shoulders. Does
the eleven-year-old stay that ladylike all the time?
So proper and uninvolved. Cindy is involved with
me; she feels she knows my head, and I know something about her. She said, of my third book, "Your
characters hold up really well." Condescending little
cunt. The girls and their mother do a jigsaw puzzle

for hours on end. I've never known jigsaw-puzzle
people.

That night another superfuck. Do we always hit
the grass right when at the point of its full aph-
rodisiac effect—or is it . . . the other stuff?

"The other stuff," she says, confidently.

She tells me about her muscles inside and how
she feels inside and what she does. "I know I have
this effect on men," she brags. "I told you the first
night I was with you, but you didn't understand."
She tells me how some guy stood her up once, and,
drunk, she told her sister, who lives nearby, that
the guy will regret it when he discovers he stood up
Karen Mason, the best fuck on the upper West Side.
Very boasty, Karen tonight.

I say: when I see you with your kids I can see
you're a very loving person and so too with me and
why shouldn't it affect your love-making style, that
side of your nature. Doesn't it? she asks. Yes, but
before you only seemed to be talking about performance.

"Some men think they can get away with the
damndest things. This one guy I met at a party recently, we left together and this girl comes with us.
She was with him. I didn't understand the situation
exactly. We got to his place and she got stoned and
fell asleep on the couch and he started making love
to me on the floor right there next to her. When

I objected he seemed surprised. I went into his bedroom and closed the door. Which also surprised him.
And then he couldn't get it up again, and then he
does, and pop he was done in ten seconds. I thought,
well, that happens sometimes. I was trying to decide
whether to stick around and I wanted to ask whether
there'd be another shot at it or whether that was
it. "Hey," I asked him, "do you like to fuck all
night sometimes?" He seemed surprised. I said, "Are
you a ten-minute-rest-in-between guy or an hour-
rest-in-between guy?" He suggested there'd be more.
So I stuck around. And there was another, but
damned if he didn't do it again the exact same way,
wham, ten seconds and he's come and it's gone down.
Shit. (She's laughing here.) A two-time loser. And
then some people come over and we got dressed and
when the people were getting ready to leave he
asked me to stay the night and I figured that, well,
I'd already sampled his stuff and there was nothing
to hang around for.

She tells me about a twenty-year-old kid she'd
been sleeping with, who'd never slept with a woman
who had an orgasm and how upset he got. "I had
to stop and reassure him that it was all right, it was
okay, and he should just continue what he was doing."

I urge her to write her sex memoirs. A dirty sex
novel from a woman's viewpoint. We discuss it.

Since women are doing 50 per cent of the fucking
going on, their viewpoint should be represented
more. She likes the idea. Write it, Karen.

Lou called me about my will. He asked me where
the divorce thing was at. I told him I didn't know,
that I hadn't spoken to my lawyer in about a month.
Why? he asked. I'll think about it and call you back,
I told him.

Karen hangs out in chic bars. She seems to prefer
young black men. I wonder if she prefers them or
whether she does it to piss her husband off even
more.

January 15, 1970. This morning Karen was changing the sheets on her gigantic bed. She put on a
fitted sheet, and without thinking of it, I took the
left side of the sheet and fitted it on. It occurred
to me around the same time it occurred to her; she
stopped and glowed at me, came over and gave me
a big kiss. "Oh, it's been such a long time since a
man helped me make my bed."

I called my agent from her place. She had just
hung up on the editor.

"He thinks it's a masterpiece. He thought it was

better than *Portnoy*. He'll make it their big book
in the fall. I asked for fifteen thousand dollars."

"Jesus, there are too many good things happening to me all of a sudden."

"Is it so hard to take?" she asks.

"It's just that so much stuff is coming in all of
a sudden."

"Isn't it a good feeling?"

"I deserve it."

"You do, yes. . . . What are you doing with yourself these days?"

"Well, I go to Yoga class, to the shrink, and
building social relations, and—"

"That's enough. How much do you have to do?"

I am in a state of pure self-indulgence. All I do
is go to the shrink, go to Yoga class, and make
love. It is enough. There is nothing else I want to
do.

from notebook five

My apartment's smallness and dinginess and back-facing, second-floor, courtyard view: I still don't like it.

The nude photographs Karen showed me of herself—very disturbing. She looked so Viva-emaciated, so diseased and bony and Buchenwald-starved, especially that one of her naked at the ironing board. She was telling a lot of Jason-husband stories, their awful courtroom scenes, the way she cries in the courtroom. Almost every weekday morning she calls her lawyer, or he calls her. Jason had spent twenty-five thousand dollars on legal fees in three years, she tells me. Once, a man told her he'd give her all the money she needed and she resented it. She said she was afraid of Leonard Cohen when she was taking his pictures for some magazine story. She felt

she could have fallen madly in love with him and
that he'd have treated her like shit and hurt her.
Cal: nobody wants to be what they grow up to be.
How come? Where are the happy childhood people?
Karen remarking on my inability to feel success and
accomplishment about a book of mine made into a
movie.

A flood in the kitchen. Evening. Several inches of
water. Plumbers running around. Molly barking.
Smells like a damp basement here. I ask the building handyman how it's going. He answers and I
don't understand him. It sounds like English but I
just don't get it. And then some girl who wants me
to invest in her boutique calls up. What does that
have to do with the flood? What do I have to do
with her boutique?

All this talk about gonorrhea all of a sudden.
Everyone seems to have had it at one time or another.
Everyone seems to know it's really a secret that
there's an epidemic of it in the East Village and
around the East Side bar scene. Karen had it and
nearly died from it two years ago.

You oughta see 1E, laughs the handyman. You
tink you got problems? It's flooded. You don't have
it so bad at all here.

I grieve for 1E. Molly is looking suspicious and
scared. She's ready to attack. The super has come.

He's dipping into the sink with a bucket and scoop-
ing out blackened water and heaving it out the window to the courtyard. The other guy is mopping the
floor and sqeezing the shmutz into the mop bucket.
Wet wires sputtering on the floor next to the refrigerator. They turn off the fuse. A flashlight. The
basement wet smell. It's like a Red Cross disaster
area in here. The handyman starts to giggle. He's
sixty, got no teeth. "Everytin's happening to us tonight, yah? Hah, hah. I haven't had such a crazy
night like this in a long. . . ." They don't smell the
grass. I have an inspiration. I light some candles
around normally used for erotic settings and illuminate the two workers. I light some incense. Then
I take out the plug to my new transistor stereo and
turn it on. Roscoe talking to the super and the handyman, telling them what's fucked up about things.
Now I know my new transistor stereo has a use.
I wondered why I got it transistorized. It's so when
the lights go out in your house because of a plumb-
ing flood you can serenade the plumbers if you have
a transistorized stereo unit such as mine. I ought to
write the Toshibo people and tell them about it.
The super is from Central America. He looks like an
Israeli paratrooper. He is saying to the handyman,
"The boyfriend of my mother-in-law needs some
money and he wants to sell his . . ." His assistant,
the sixty-year-old freight elevator operator, is howl-
ing. The Beatles playing now on WNEW: "Good

Day Sunshine." This is a very mysterious scene here
now. Even Molly's got her ears way up like she's
listening to it all but she can't quite get it. Now
they're fucking with the fuses. The handyman is
grinning. He has more going for him than his job
but I don't know what. They turn the lights on.
Time for them to go downstairs and check out the
water level there. "I got a headache, you know?"
says the super to the handyman as they head out
the door together.

  Now, Ellie, whose mother died and left her a for-
tune. A big round red-cheeked girl who paints. Big-
bosomed and upper-classy. She recently bought a
hundred-acre farm in upstate New York. We go to
the same shrink. She is the girl I met at the party
at Casey's house, the girl who thought I looked so
different from last October. A Philadelphia girl. We
make love fairly well. Her big roundness turns me
on. She says I turn her on, like a teeny-bopper.
Aren't rich upper-classy girls supposed to be flat-
chested? A very well-cushioned girl.
  She has been seeing Janet for three years. She
says, "Janet knows so much about me that I don't
feel the least paranoid sleeping with you." I, on the
other hand, find it fascinating to sleep with someone who sees the same shrink I do. Maybe she can
provide Janet with a whole new clue to me and
that will be good. And even if nothing therapeuti-

cally constructive comes out of it, I nonetheless enjoy making it with Ellie. I tell her she has a decided aristocratic air about her, a coolness. She knows, and feels it separates her from people and makes her different. A fine, understandable dream about Ellie caressing my ass and me liking it. I used to hate it when Paula touched my ass; couldn't stand to be touched there.

Janet was cool about my sleeping with one of her other patients. I couldn't tell what she thought, and had no idea what Ellie told her. A little cat-and-mouse-ish. Why not? seemed to be her attitude. She didn't set it up. A coincidence.

Ellie: I can feel your curiosity. It's very appealing. It's like you're just surfacing.

Arnie: If the grass opens you up and loosens you a bit and you can be more honest in yourself and in your writing, then go ahead and smoke. Be glad for it instead of worrying about it.

He is a graduate school student in psychology. Last year he worked as a surrogate father in a far-out, experimental asylum in Pennsylvania. Divorced. Maintains a strange friendship with his ex-wife who moved to California.

Grass seems to cover up the discomfort of my flu-cold-virus-whatever. Pain-killing medicinal properties of *Cannabis*, scientists are reporting.

Arnie: You've been into reading. I haven't read a novel in seven years, since *To Kill a Mockingbird*. Reading is a tremendous investment in time. It's done alone, sitting still, and is a very passive activity. That's why I don't read much. (Jesse: I haven't finished a book in two months, since *The French Lieutenant's Woman*. Since I started reading, in childhood, that's probably the longest time I've ever gone without finishing a book.)

I am feeling run-down from this ongoing cold-flu-virus-whatever. Do I sleep poorly in all these girls' beds? Probably. Is the amount of grass I've been smoking bad for my . . . health?

Why was Karen so distant and ignoring last night?

I feel a little useless today.

Janet says my mother continues to intimidate me, that I still have these whining phone conversations with her. She still wants her way with you. She will continue trying to control you, trying to make you feel bad, make you comply. She won't loosen her hold. But you can loosen your hold, says Janet.

Did I write fictions, constructions of life, so as to hide my real self and feelings? Or was I flirting with finding out about me?

When will I ever be able to read my books over again?

Karen went off on a really incredibly heavy Jason trip, telling me Jason-horror-divorce stories, one after the next, for an hour or so, like it was hypnotic and uncontrollable, until, gently as I could I said, "Hey, please stop."

Today, Monday, I'm supposed to have lunch with the new editor downtown, at some fancy restaurant.

To call someone at midnight is a very provocative, erotic act. Ellie calls me at midnight to ask if I'm busy, and comes over, and we make it in the dark. She doesn't like sleeping alone. Insomniacal. Watches TV till dawn.

Karen tells me that she still sleeps with Richard, her black revolutionary boyfriend, but informs me that when she is with him she spends most of her time talking about me. So I told her (guilt, reciprocity, whatever) that I made it with some girl late last night. This is confusing to me. And a little insane-making. Doesn't anyone really feel jealous in all this? Neither me nor Karen nor Richard nor Ellie nor Ellie's boyfriend-for-four-years, the famous painter? Or is everyone pretending? Karen says: "Jesse, I don't feel bad when you see someone else. I think it's lovely that other women can know you that way." Is that to be believed? Is there no such thing as possessiveness or jealousy for her? Or is it a pose? It saddens me somehow. It's too cool this way. Karen says I'm acting out something like she's Paula and I'm rubbing her nose in the fact I sleep

with Ellie. (Yet she, Karen, is always telling me
Jason-horror stories and fucking black guys. So who's
hung up about reacting against who?)

The other day Tommy asked me what the Beatles
mean when they sing about doing it in the road. I
explained about ambiguity, and kissing in public.

Sometimes I look back over a couple of days and
can't recall what happened. Janet broke an appointment on Friday. My phone went out of order. The
supervisor I called from outside kept calling my
phone "an instrument." I went to Ellie's house to
make calls in the afternoon, and then made it with
her. An hour after leaving her house I am at Karen's,
and after dinner and a movie, I make it with her,
about five hours after leaving Ellie's. Somehow,
goddamit, that bothers me.

Tommy at Ellie's house, building with Tinkertoys
and drawing with crayons to the music of "Straw-
berry Fields" and "Penny Lane." How beautiful to
be raised on Beatles music.

I need one night's sleep sleeping alone. No midnight phone calls from Ellie. Sleep alone! I'll never
get rid of this fucking cold otherwise.

I bought two new pair of pants without much
trouble. And I like both pants.

Ellie's telling me again about sleeping with her old

boyfriend alternate nights: how do I feel about it? Ambivalent and confused, even after I've talked about it with Janet. So my parents were super-possessive of me, and I was super-possessive of Paula, and now I'm not supposed to be possessive. But somehow when you're fucking a girl you like and in the middle of it you have to think of someone else's cock in there, a few hours ago, where yours is now, it can kind of turn you off. It's that visceral a reaction. Or maybe it shouldn't turn you off; maybe it should turn you on. No, that's perverse. A very confusing subject. I've been thinking a lot about it these days.

It looks like Terry will be next. A baby-sitter—au pair who lives partly with Sally's friends, George and Margaret. So beautiful it's hard to believe. A Victorian Old World voluptuousness. An angelic apple-cheek country-fresh complexion. A luscious, full mouth, a chiseled nose, soft and loving brown eyes, an enormous, enormous chest, a softness of skin at the neck and chest that I like and hope to like more. . . . I have no idea what world she lives in. She *feels* so much different from Karen's lean, hard flanks—the bulk of her hips, her deep, soft, mysterious roundness. She has a quality of mysteriousness about her, too. I could sit and write poetry about her, if she posed as though for a painting. I never did that. Would she do it?

Holy shit! They came through with a twenty-thousand-dollar advance for my novel! He must think this book is some kind of fucking master-piece, or some potential best-seller thing. Or else they're nuts or something to pay me all that money for something I wrote. It is four times as much as my last advance. God bless them and I hope they make it back. They must be planning to, since I don't believe this is tendered in the form of a grant.

What will I do with the money this time? A farm, undoubtedly, this time. And we will see what happens from there. They would like to have a forty-thousand-dollar paperback sale to break even, but they want to do more than break even. How do they figure they'll be able to do that with this book? Isn't it hard to read? It doesn't seem *popular* to me. Why do they think they can reach so many people with it? Why would it be of any interest to anybody? Doesn't everyone know I'm crazy?

Annie and Saul are suddenly destroying each other. Their marriage has ended. They can't get stopped what they're doing to each other. They haven't slept together in months. She plots out a chart that will keep them together till June when she has a Master's degree. She'll never last that long.

Annie said she didn't understand how when I was
there *why* and *how* I got up out of bed in the morning, got up and kept going, how I made the effort
and went through the motions. She said her thing
is to stop functioning, to stay in bed for two or three
weeks and have hallucinations. She was popping
pills, she said. Any pills. She said she would try to
reach me when I was staying there and it bounced
up against an invisible shield and wouldn't penetrate me, that nothing entered me from outside. She
says she used to try a lot.

I brought the kids back and she opens the door
stark naked. "Hi," she says, "did you have a good
time?" The bathroom-bathtub in the kitchen–living
room of her apartment. She gets into the bathtub,
steamy hot, while I take the kids' clothes off, and
telling me how the Panthers kicked her out of their
meeting house because they were tired of hearing her
tell them that if they quit eating meat and ate only
brown rice their problems would be over. Kicked her
ass out. Food would change their heads and they'd
see their whole thing with the pigs differently. Asks
questions as to the nature of my sex life, from within
the bathtub. Kids on the floor eating rice out of
balls with their fingers. Smoking a cigarette three or
four feet from the bathtub, sitting in a rocker. We
discuss Yoga, a mutual friend, why our five-year-old

son is not in kindergarten, why I will not have them
for the summer unless I and my then-girlfriend cook
them brown rice and cereal foods each day, how
their good health demands my compliance.

She stands up full-length to wash her hair and
faces me directly. I remark how she still looks pretty
much like last summer, a little thinner, more angu-
lar. "And flexible," she adds. "I've gotten more flexible, in my body and my spirit."

We discuss movies, *M*A*S*H*, why it was unwise
to spit on restaurant floors, how all her friends get
church chits for five dollars a week worth of gro-
ceries.

She dries herself. She does not put on a bathrobe.
She crosses in front of me to shake the rice on the
stove. She runs ten errands across my path, inches
away. My hands never leave their pockets. Her figure is far inferior to the women I've been spending
my time with lately; so is her behavior. After the
twelfth or thirteenth trip past me, all but tickling
my ear with her ass as she passes me, she puts on a
robe.

She offers me hot cider.

I accept.

She stirs up some brown rice.

"Hey," she points, "did you see my candle? The
red candle?"

"Where?" I ask.

She points.

On a shelf is a red candle in the shape of an erect penis, a wick at the top.

"Some friends of mine did it. They're really into stuff like that. It's just the right size."

"It's sadistic, or sado-sexual, or something."

"What? Why?"

"How do you feel when you light it and you watch a penis burning down?"

"Oh come on, I'm just into it because of the aesthetics."

On finishing the cider, I get up, "Well, I'm going."

I head for the bathtub and kiss the kids before I go. I see the Chinese fur hat I loaned to Paula. I realize I am annoyed she hasn't returned it in a month. I remove the hat from atop a box, and kiss the kids.

Paula removes the hat from my hand.

I turn around. "Let's have the hat."

She turns and puts it in a drawer, closing it.

I head for the drawer.

"Will you stop this shit and give me the hat?"

"I don't have any other hat," she says. "My ears are cold."

I put my hand on the drawer and give a tug and feel the pressure of her legs against the drawer.

"You've got two other hats," I tell her.

The foolishness of the thing. It hits me. Why am I playing this game bent over at the drawer. "Look,

get away from the fucking drawer right now."
Doesn't budge. Steadfastly looking me in the eye.
Little does she know I am a new man. "I'm not
playing this shit with you any more, Paula." She
stands firm. I take her by the upper arm and shove
her out of the way. I open the drawer and remove
the object of the attention.

"You're an *animal,* Jesse." I say nothing. "You're
not seeing the kids next weekend," she hisses. "Over
this hat?" "You're an animal. You eat meat. You'll
always be an animal." Tommy is now crying. "I'm
not bringing them up," she says. "Well, if I'm not
going to see them next weekend and you want me
to cook brown rice for them all summer or else I
won't see them then I'll keep this." I take a white
envelope containing a hundred-dollar check off the
table. "Keep your fucking money. I don't need it.
Just get out of here."

I kiss the kids and depart.

Depart.

Wondering to what unhealthy fate am I consign-
ing them with her? Wondering whether she's not
more like an Orthodox Jewish lady with her food
restrictions than I've appreciated. That I provoked
her by staying there while she provoked me by dancing around liberated naked, that I didn't have to
sit and stay for that scene but felt cool and objective
and it was worth validating because it frees me
of unpleasant wonderings about her. That the shock

of grabbing her by the arm and thrusting her aside must have been considerable and degrading.

A telephone conversation with Karen:
She said she felt trapped into a role she wasn't happy with. She claims I encouraged her to present me with her experiences with other men. I was re-doing something I had done with my wife, and more-over it was stupid for me to tell her, when I couldn't see her because she was busy one night, "Karen, you're driving me to other women." It's perfectly obvious, she continues, that there are other ways to say you have other relationships. That seemed vi-cious and provocative, she says. It has nothing to do with a specific girl, a specific person, she goes on; it's something you do with people, Jesse. (I had called for a post-mortem. She had been avoiding me.)

It makes me feel a kind of possessiveness you have toward me. It gives me no room to breathe. I can't be that restricted. (She has to be with a different man every other night, only *she* doesn't know it, just like she's telling me things about *me* that I don't know.) Jealousy is a problem, she continues. There's no dignity in such possessiveness. That's what mar-riages are about, for heaven's sake. And it's too bad, Jesse, because I enjoyed your company so much. Your jealousy and possessiveness business can be erased by successful psychoanalysis, and it's too bad

it's not done with now, because there's something
in you I really like.

Tell you the truth, I used you, I told you more
about myself than I usually tell other men. You
just stood there and listened. You have a selective
grid. Your ability to respond to me was very finely
tuned.

I don't think you recognize positive transference
when it's thrown at you. You refuse to see and ac-
knowledge positive feelings coming out of someone
for you. I could see it was there and I didn't have
to worry about it.

There's not much difference in your books between
you, the voices. In terms of the way you describe
people and their relating. A quality of standing outside and looking. An underlying frantic feeling that
people are always like that and they never break
through. You're always watching for a moment and
it never comes. You use current things in the society
as a kind of manual of despair. There's no peace.
Like providence has conspired to torment you.

Karen is a very sophisticated lady. She's thirty-
nine.

I'm reading Rollo May's *Love and Will,* she said.
Take care.
You too.

January 27. A long phone conversation with
George. He called from Vermont the other day and

left a message for me to call. I never got him. In
the city they told me what they found.

The farm demands a one-third down payment. It
was harder to see more than five farms a day. There
were two possibilities, they both thought. One was
almost all timberland, very wooded, an old, old
small house with a funny addition on it. The house
was livable. With 260 acres. Some open areas. A
valley and a brook running through it. He'd make
a pond, he says. A loan from Margaret's father,
maybe. He wouldn't build. Her brother would want
to build if he went into it with them. Do organic
food.

Very medieval, the money thing, he says. That
much usury. With interest it's $72,000. It costs
$45,000 if you can just pay for it.

Margaret: It's on the top of a mountain!

The house has three bedrooms upstairs.

There might be some teasing about Billy's long
hair up there. You remember that time in Milwau-
kee, George? Look mommy, this little kid yells to his
mother. Hippies. Ycchh. Fuck. The poor kid was
programmed.

Molly is looking very insecure. She refuses to shit.
She got into Ellie's garbage.

"Have you been neglecting her?" Ellie asks.
"When a dog looks like it's having emotional dif-

ficulties, it's often because the master is in trouble,"
says her.

I didn't get it up for Ellie that day. Odd.

At three o'clock today Terry broke the date for
tonight, saying she had to baby-sit for Margaret.
A blow. I was looking forward to tonight. Am I
receiving mild discouragement from Terry? Or mild
encouragement. When did it start with her?

I still can't believe my publisher came through
with a twenty-thousand-dollar advance. That's an
incredible amount of money.

Condensation is needed here and there. I am involved in cutting. Lines are gone and going that
no one will ever know about. Turns of phrase lost.
But needed, I hope.

Mansfield asks why the threat from China seems
to appear, disappear and reappear, periodically.
From the White House. The Pentagon worriers.
White House still concerned over Chinese nuclear
capability.

Nixon's a fag. Someone the other day was telling
me how he knew Nixon's California shrink, a guy
who specialized in treating big-deal fags, politicians
and movie stars. He claims to have failed with Dick.

Tomorrow's headline: President Sues Writer Who
Calls Him a Fag.

So *what* if the President is a fag?

Cronkite and Huntley are worried over encroachments on the freedom of the press. Justice Department subpoenas and such. They better be worried.

Right now Ellie is the only one. The pattern has been a few days of that before someone else sets in, in this case it'll be Terry, I hope. Then, according to my chart, I fuck the two at the same time for a week or ten days, and drop woman A and continue alone with woman B and then find someone after a week alone with woman B, say, woman C, who I fuck with woman B for a week or so, and then drop woman B. And so on. It's had five such cycles now in two months.

Heartbeat very speeded up right now, all you other drug fiends out there, all over, whoever, with your own speeded-up heartbeats.

Ellie has a very big body. Heavy and rolling. She loves to make love. I have no possessiveness thing with her at all. We like each other just enough, the right amount, so that nobody feels attached, attacked or damaged by the other people. Big, soft rolling hills of tits. Terry looks even bigger. Hey Paula baby, I'm into big, soft rolling hills of tits, for all those years of deprivation with you. Cunt. Will she ever grow up and do something about herself? Call the lawyer and tell him to put something in about her working after a certain point. Like a

year or two hence. "Why should I work?" she cries
all the time. Because it's good for your dignity, and
you wouldn't know about that because you don't
have any dignity.

I think my lawyer understands me. Who is he? I
don't know who he is, I realize. I wonder if after
this divorce shit we can be friends.

Four to six inches of new snow in New Hampshire.

Writing helps validate your experience and your
existence. You can read back and say, "That's
where I was then. That's what I was doing."

Would the publisher be doing this big deal on
the book if I had succeeded in killing myself in
July and the thing would have to come out post-
humously. No, someone would have had to decipher
the first draft. Who would have done it? Paula?
My father? My father would have been embarrassed
and worried. What about my agent? My father
would definitely be ashamed of it. Paula would
know what to do with it. But would it have been
her right? Morbid.

A disaster meeting Douglas O'Reilly, Ellie's long-
time boyfriend, the one she felt married to. The
painter.

Then Terry.

Ahh, Terry.

Terry fits some of the description of my hero's

imagined mistress in the last book. Like Botticelli's Venus stepping out of the scallop. Dark, dark hair that frizzes out at the sides while hanging fluffy and netty. A big, big body.

Incredible open-mouthed joy of her while we're doing it. Ruby port lips. Her immense breasts flopping the other way when she stands on her head. Skin like the soft surface of brushed chamois suede. A lovable girl, whereas Ellie is likable.

Terry's father a shrink, in California. He's got a picture of Freud hanging over his toilet, she says. Or maybe it's Jung, come to think of it, she reflects. And maybe it's over the sink, not the toilet.

She made walnuts and prunes in brandy sauce for an after-it snack.

"I just knew I'd like making it with you," she said. "I had thought you might be really into it."

The calm smile on her lips as she sleeps.

Her red cheeks.

A square Scandinavian beauty of a jaw. A big girl. Nakedly she carries a lot of pride. Dimension. And a lot of mysticism. With humor. Fanciful mind. Astrologically oriented.

Bleeding in the streets, because of the pill, she says. Doctor puts her on the pill at fifteen in California, to help keep her skin free of pimples.

Her composure bothers me sometimes. She wants to have kids, loves them, wants the right man first.

Fairly quiet at love, and after she said, *That* was

like *very* unusual for a first encounter. And she laughed.

I'm glad to see you here, I said, waking up in the morning.

I'm glad to see *you*, she whispered back.

She's disturbed her sister has so much more pubic hair than she. I got the tits, she said.

What a face! It's enough to make me write poetry. She thinks her face is lopsided. She puts down her accident of genetics.

I thought that once I laid hands on you I wouldn't be able to stop, I told her.

Light dances out of her soft brown eyes when she smiles. When I tell her that, she smiles. More light.

Men are always lusting after me, she says.

She was a little afraid I'd find her fat and not like her body. Her mind she knew I got, she says. She wants to lose ten pounds and she tells me how much nicer she'll look. How much nicer can she possibly look?

I'd like to make love to you in tall grass during the summer.

California grass? she asks.

Why?

It's sharp and prickly. She laughs. More light.

Paula once emitted lots of light for me. It diminished. I helped diminish it. Paula is condemned to repeating the mistakes of her past. Aren't we all?

Better emit my own light. Safer than relying on someone else's light.

She's no superfuck. Quiet at it. Gentle.

I like the way her head goes. Its fancies and flights and metaphysical, ethereal wonderings, about space and changes and one's soul transferences. Which reality is real? she'll ponder. Both. She absolutely knocks me cold with some of her mind-wonderings-aloud. So convoluted it's hard to follow, hard to recall to write them down. A good flip-floppy mind.

Yeahhhhh, she says slowly.

She talks a lot like a certain heroine I know.

Once, the story has reached her, Sally called me and I wasn't feeling up to it, sick or something, and I am reputed to have said. "The only person I'd have the energy to fuck right now is Terry." So Sally told Margaret and Margaret told Terry who in bed told me, asking, "Is Sally good in bed?"

I sure kiss her a lot. I like to kiss her. I like the feel of her surfaces. With those places of just the right tantalizing amount of soft and childish fuzz-down. Her sister has wiry, beardlike hairs around the perimeter of her nipples—as did Karen—and that puts her sister uptight.

She certainly seemed happy in the morning, and meaning it, when she said: "I sure had a nice time last time, the dinner and after and everything."

At noon, finally emerging and walking through the snow-covered factory streets of West Broadway, arms around each other. The feel of her just where her big ass starts to flare out, at the base of her spine.

But I wanted to feel better when I saw you. Like I just didn't want to feel sick. It was just being sensible.

Yes.

It's so great to have a man touch your breasts, she whispers.

And her clavicles. And her baby-smooth skin.

You'll probably marry someone who's divorced and has a kid or two, someone who's already been through it, she says.

Nicole: Just so long as when you're with me you're nice to me.

Men tell me I'm too fectionate. Do you think I'm too fectionate? If you do, just say so.

Are you going to make me come?

I only got liberated recently. . . . Yesterday.

I never do things like this, when I just meet someone for the first time. A couple of hours later. Bam.

I'd been going with this guy for three months. He was very gentle. Very kind. Do you want to know what went wrong? Are you interested at all?

What went wrong?
He's a she?
What? You're a dike?
Haven't you ever met one?
Never slept with one.
Oh! How could you? How could you believe I'm
a lesbian? How awful!

You look a little spaced out. Are you taking drugs
for your cold?
What would you say, Nicole replied, if I told you
I took acid three hours ago.
That would explain it.
Well—I did.
Now that I look at you, it makes sense. I can see
it.
Oh I didn't take *acid*. Did you really believe me?

Why does Nicole do those things? She's been in
analysis for three years. Shuffle-gaited, long-legged,
very furry pubis. Quiet whimpers, like a puppy in
love. Timid. Still.

Terry.
I am shy. You're right. Still am.
I'm still trying to puzzle out your karma, Jesse.

You've got a child's inquisitiveness. A child's curiosity.

Where someone's head is at is of very great concern to Terry.

Her smile is slow and gradual and big. It doesn't just click on. It spreads. She liked *M*A*S*H*. We went to see it together. So many people stare at her on the street.

She played the violin when she was a kid. So did Karen and so do her three girls.

I keep the radio on, playing rock music, almost the entire time I'm in the house, whether I'm alone or with someone.

I'm very happy when I'm with her.

She makes love in the same gentle shy way she is. Her orgasm is quiet. Why is that ecstasy only limited to the orgasm? Why is it the only act that sends it off? Terry's answer: I have a feeling it's probably chemical.

She made the bed, with blanket, unlike the others; a practical girl.

Her bikini knocked them out at Fire Island last year. I'll bet.

Dylan was a very big influence on her life, she says.

A match crisis. All empty books. She gets up, pauses, and then heads for one book, opens it, and then smiles. There were matches in it. How did you know? I ask. Get to know me and you'll see: I'm *truly* psychic. When George and Margaret lose

something I can find it all the time. I have knowledge of their sequences. I know where to find it,
where they'd have left it.

She relies a good deal on intuition. A quiet observer. An astrology bug. A Scorpio. A California
love-child. She's twenty. I'm thirty-three.

The tolerance to grass must be building. I've
smoked every night since the beginning of December.
About two months, every night, with five or six
exceptions, a cold. I scarcely get high any more. I
will skip a couple of days.

Why did I sleep with three different girls three
nights in a row? It was exhausting. Once Friday
night with Nicole, once Saturday morning with Nicole; once Saturday night with Ellie, and twice Sunday night with Terry. The only one I was really into
was Terry.

No calls from my parents lately.

Grass is a hypo. It hypos everything, including
the quality of the creamy sculptings you make in
Haagen-Dazs ice cream. A word of praise and support for the Haagen-Dazs people, for their boysen-

berry, their chocolate, their coffee, their vanilla and rum raisin.

Mailed the letter to my parents. Read once Kafka wrote a sixty-page letter to his father and never mailed it. I mailed my twelve pages after keeping the letter in a drawer for a week.

Dragged up a lot of the old crap again; put in black and white maybe it'll be clearer to them. Angry tones. A lot about going numb to survive with them. Tried to tell them about *their* craziness, how I became such an exhibitionist in my work because they made me hide everything as a child. About life not just being random acts, of repeating the same sick, unhealthy ways of dealing with a person or a situation. About how they ignored each other and fought with each other, alternating; about their fears and the fears they put into me. Requested exchange of vault keys and such. Told them that having hid themselves from me in life, I must pass up the opportunity of picking over their papers and effects and discovering who they were after they're gone. Said over and over, maybe too many times, that I am not doing this to hurt them, the way they take all the things I've done, but to try to tell them what has been so wrong between us. I'm not sure what prompted my writing them. I think it was that formal, official note I got from my mother a little while ago—its legal sound, its

coldness and distance, as though written from one
stranger to another.

Why are all three girls I am going out with doctors' daughters?

Terry: You are one of the two or three men I've
known with whom I feel a real sexual communion.
Which is it? Two or three?

Apples. I never saw them her way. Cut in cross
section. This way the core doesn't exist. She dis-
covered it once when she was eating an apple as
a child. She does it with pear and zucchini and
bananas. The apple in cross-section slices has a five-
sided star in its middle, which evolves and dissolves
as you keep cutting. She can carve fruit like no
one I've ever known. She triangularized a banana
in cross section for me. Amazing feats.

She seems a little stoned and spaced out all the
time. She says she seems and feels far away sometimes. A little dreamy and slow. I loved the look
on her face when I beckoned her and she came over.
It sometimes takes a lot of energy to get into other
people, she says. Sometimes it takes all my energy
to stay with myself, she adds. She says I have a
New York City mystique. It's about living too long

a time in New York. She analyzes it. What it means
is that you're used to functioning with a lot of other
people's vibrations, electrical binds. I feel certain
responsibilities she doesn't, she thinks. Maybe unconsciously, she allows. I have greater feeling of
greater care about something.

A greater sense of cruciality, she clarifies.

The apple is the fruit of the flowering plant, a
five-petaled flower.

She treats herself very gently. It's something I
can learn a lot from.

A dream from Tuesday afternoon's nap. February
10. I am sick and feverish. Paula is there. She asks
if I would like my brow and neck cooled with a
sponge. I can't decide. I want it done, but not by
her. I don't answer. She mops my brow. Oh how
good it feels, but I am torn. I like the feeling, but
I wish someone else were doing it, not her.

I ask you, all things considered and nonetheless,
to be of good cheer.

My Yoga classes end with the leader's blessing:
"May the entire world be filled with peace and
joy."

Why is this lovely red-cheeked girl so reserved and flat a lover? It's disconcerting. She reminds Arnie of a pioneer-frontier girl. She reminds others of Israeli army girls, kibbutz girls, mystic-hippies. Why are her hands so cold when they touch my cock? Why are her big tits so cold? Why doesn't she cry out when she comes? Why does she only breathe a little fast? She says to me: Your karma I am trying to puzzle out always. You have the bemused observer part and the child part. Is she frigid and promiscuous? Maybe the last time was bad because I was disgusted with the amount of blood between my legs, all over my cock and stuck to the hairs of my thighs.

She got off the pill and got a coil put in this morning. She is very upset. She sounds a little hysterical. She won't see me. She is with George and Margaret.

VIII

from notebook five

"Why do I trust you?" Lisa asked in the morning. I haven't hurt you yet, I offered. A day later it occurred to me: why do *I* trust *her?*

On Friday night a party in a 96th Street brownstone. Five hundred people circulating in and out of six apartments, in the hallways, on the staircases, on plastic furniture, sitting on the floor. Secretaries, teachers, Jewish Guild for the Blind girls, CIA girls, hippies and straights, but mostly straights in weekend hippie clothes. A subway kind of party. Pipes and grass sweetening the room with plastic furniture. Dazed-looking girls. Couples necking in the corner. Cops thumping up the stairs and glancing in at twenty people on the floor. Someone flashes a V-sign. A Fellini party without the bizarre people.

A lot of aggressive girls. A lot of aggressive guys. One girl ran up to me and said, "Oh save me, there's an awful man over there. He just walked right up to me and said, 'Hey, d'ya smell as good below the waist as above?'"

Next day, Valentine's Day, Saturday, two o'clock outside wandering. Trying to clear my head. Went to the New Yorker bookstore. Opened my eyes to a very pretty girl at the Psychology section. White-skinned, dark-haired. She was holding Konrad Lorenz. *On Aggression*. Why don't I remember what I first said to her? We talked about Lorenz, Freud, analysis, Sullivanians. Her father a shrink. Another one! Reich. Intuition. Schizophrenia. How do you feel intuitively about having coffee with me downstairs? Red cheeks and little dangly earrings and her mother's old mouton coat or something. Green sweater and jeans. Very sexy and ladylike. Starks for coffee. And two hours on drugs and her sister and college. She is Lisa and she is twenty-two and so pretty I couldn't stop looking at her. Lisa. Boston. Baby-sitting tonight. She lives two blocks away.

If you have dinner with me I bet I could find you a replacement baby-sitter.

We go to my apartment. A flurry of phone calls for baby-sitters. Her looking around my apartment, playing with Molly. Dinner at The Cellar.

Snowy evening. The snow seemed unbelievably

white, whiter and sparkling prettier than I'd ever
seen it. I kept saying how nice the snow looked.

When I walked the dog and returned for Lisa at
her apartment on 84th Street, she had changed her
clothes. Her hair was down. She wore a dress. Looked
like a different girl.

Hey, you look different!

She can look Irish, French, Spanish, German,
Italian. And Jewish.

Light dances in her eyes when she smiles. Really
does.

She has the kind of serene beauty that makes men
turn to look at her when she walks into a room.
Only she doesn't know it.

She looked elegant at dinner, spare ribs for her
and pepper steak for me.

She tells me about the apartment in the Bronx
where friends and acquaintances become dealers and
junkies, and how she got the hell out of there. She
went to NYU uptown. She has an eighteen-year-
old sister who at fourteen got arrested for being
naked on the beach at Provincetown with a twenty-
two-year-old guy. The sister recently started a half-
way house for unhappy kids in Boston who can't
live at home with their parents. Back home for
grass, music, Haagen-Dazs. Once I kissed her I
couldn't stop. On it went, and on, and a beautifully
womanly lover. How could she only be twenty-two

and make love like that? I could love this one. She
scares me a little. I scare her, too. She sees a shrink
four days a week. We make it twice. So very responsive, so active and delighted, the way her mouth
opens wide and she throws her head back and breaks
into an ecstatic laugh, a cry before and during and
after. A tender girl, an affective girl, a responsive
girl, and a terribly good necker and a passionate
inventive mouth. A good fit. A girlish uninhibited-
ness. Womanly. Lisa Bergson.

Spent every night with her, at her place and mine,
ten days in a row. We eat out, at my place, at hers.
She made herself available to me, and I to her. I
decided not to stagger her with another girl. I decided not to program my social life and not to protect myself. She is very agreeable. She is very sweet
and soft.

I called her every night between six and seven,
after Yoga class. Are you studying Tantric Yoga?
she asked. It's got something to do with sexual performance.

She went away with me for the weekend. We
were supposed to go hear the Swami speak but—
she likes holy people—instead we made pork chops
and got stoned and went to see a movie about a
donkey, *Au Hasard Balthazar*. The unconscious re-
placed the conscious and memory failed. I don't
know what the movie was about. On Saturday
rented a Ford Galaxie and drove to Woodstock to

pick up the kids and go to Elaine's farm in New
Jersey.

I try to remember what you're like when I'm
not with you, how you look, how you speak, and I
think, about sex, "Oh Jesse, he's a dynamite lover."
I really dig your kids. Tommy is so sensitive to
other people and to his own feelings. Suzie is so
bright.

Tommy: I like Lisa. I'm getting to know her better.

Lisa: I can take care of other people, but not myself.

Donald Barthelme is a computer, she says. I'd
like to write that as graffiti all over town. Would
anyone understand?

Paula at Woodstock: I'll swap you a Tim Leary
book and an astrology book for *Stalking the Wild
Asparagus*. Are you interested in astrology, Lisa?
I used to be, Lisa replies.

Lisa Bergson is a superfuck.

When are you going to find me boring, she asks.

We have a fine communication when we're making love. She laughs and cries out. On my knees.
She arches her back, weight on her shoulders, eye-
balls swimming and glassy, crotch rubbing up and
down with mine, not in and out. Ready to faint.
At the end her mouth wide open, ovaled, eyes
clenched and urging me on.

I've been so immersed in your life, she says. You
don't know as much about mine.

Her friends at NYU were a lot of acid-heads,
speed freaks and junkies. Dealers, too. "They
thought it was like status to be doing junk—you
know, that's *really* suffering."

Listening to *The Cream.* Doing "Train Time."
The harmonica and drums. Just lying and listen.

Toward the end of the drum solo: I think I'm going
to have an orgasm, she says. I mean it. Her eyes
close, her breathing quickens.

Sometimes my sexual drive frightens people off,
she says.

I may be getting a prostate infection or urethritis
or something. And she's a week late with her period.

Maybe I'm just a good fuck, she says.
Maybe I'm just a good fuck for you, I say.
Maybe, she says.

Hey, something's happening.

I love watching her undress. I find you very beautiful to look at. Do you know that?
She giggles.

Here we are again, she says afterward, lying with
her head on my arm.
Listen, I tell her, I really have other things to

do with my time. I can't just make love to you all
the time.

Rrrright on.

She goes to her shrink four times a week. For the
last three years.

How do the Beatles keep doing it?

She was nervous about meeting Paula. The kids
looked fine, although Tommy was crying and crawl-
ing under the house when I got there. Nissim there.
Suzie calls Nissim "Ni-Ni." Tommy had on a red ny-
lon parka. Paula gave me Wheatena, rice crackers
and Kokoh for the kids. The cabin was on the side of
an icy hill five miles outside Woodstock. It was freezing. It had a kerosene stove. It was about ten feet by
twelve feet. Posters on the wall of Swami Satchidananda, two other swamis, Indians fucking, Panthers
with fists clenched. On the floor cushions and pil-
lows and blankets and mats and sleeping bags.

A four-hour drive across southern New York State
and northern New Jersey to Elaine's farm. Near the
Delaware Water Gap. Just as it was getting dark.
Putting stuff away. Toys and clothes and food. Molly
ecstatic with the outdoors. A big floating American

supercar. Doesn't make you tired driving long distances. Changed Suzie's diaper. Tommy fell down
the stairs.

For dinner we had yoghurt and pumpernickel and
yellow cheese and scrambled eggs and hamburgers
and rice and bananas. The kids ate and ate and ate.

A bath for Tommy and Suzie after dinner, each
reeking of piss. (I bathe them once a week at the
Ashram, said Paula at Woodstock.) Pots in the water.
Tom dumping water on his head. Suzie giggling.
Too hot, she says. Then, later, too cold.

Stories read. To bed. They slept in bunk beds.
(They had been sleeping together in the same sleeping bag.) Tommy on top, Suzie below. Suzie didn't
like the bed. She cried a lot. "Mommiya! Paula!"
*Paula's not here. Jesse's here. Daddy's here. Tommy
is here.* Tommy reassures her, too. It's all right,
Suzie, it's all right. Jesse is here.

To bed.

Stoned in front of the fireplace. Not a bad fire
either.

I go into the kids' room again. Tommy is on the
floor with Molly. He looks surprised. Molly darts
out.

He climbs back into the bed.

Good night, I say.

We kiss and hug.

I go out for two Oreos and an apple. I return
with his good night present. His face lights up, sit-

ting there at eye level on the upper bunk. I go out. Five minutes later he calls me. The apple core. "Hey, would you like to come out and see the fire?" Sure, sure. Okay.

He comes out, a little foggy, and sees the fire. His face sparkles into a big smile. He looks at Lisa lying on the couch and shares his joy with her. We sit down in front of the fire and talk, of Paula, of animal-foods, how we're all animals, how he gets tired of helping her, how we don't see each other enough, how I'm going to write children's books soon, how someone said he was stupid because he liked to wear costumes, how much he loved me, how much I loved him, how to make a good fire, why he thought Paula hated the Beatles now and called them mother-fuckers, what the word "guilty" means, how it feels to be gassed, why it's not good to tell someone you're smart (the smart people will know each other). Lying on the floor, kissing, sometimes sitting in my lap staring at the fire. Lisa ten feet behind us lying on the couch.

Back to bed, with hugs and kisses and assurances of love.

In the living room. "Did all that seem strange?" I ask.

It was very nice, she says.

Fifteen minutes later I went back for another look. He was asleep. His foot hanging over the bed.

Looking at him and Suzie, I choke, tears catch in my throat. They're so real. What a fucked-up year they're having. I'd like to take them away from Paula. Tommy is cynical of her. Suzie needs her though. Suzie needs Tommy too. I remember the night a year ago coming from the movies at night when I wouldn't stop at Paula's dealer-friend for more and Paula pissed and packing and I went into the kids' room and cried over the possibility of such a loss.

The next day, in the morning, Suzie singing Hare rama, Hare Krishna. (Having awoken once in the night, crying.) Tommy wanting breakfast. Bowls of Cheerios they eat, and Wheatena and eggs and cider. We fly kites and lose strings and kites fly away over the hill. We climb and go on the swings and play soccer. We fool with the tape recorder and make noises, tell stories. He takes pictures with his camera. We examine ice crystals. Suzie says, "Suzie come." We buy toys—mechanical dogs, a doll, a musical pull-toy, more kites, a clay-modeling set. We get red faces outdoors. Lisa, says Tommy, is pretty nice.

Baths again, and he gives me and Lisa shampoos. He loves to spill lots of water on our heads. Suzie giggles. She climbs onto the bed we're resting on, and bounces and laughs uproariously. Tommy too. Who is Suzie? She's strange. Do I love her?

"Paula says the Beatles are too noisy," Tommy says.

"Do you think their music is beautiful?"

"Yes! Yes! Noisy but beautiful."
Paula is a runaway child running wild.

At the end of the weekend, Monday, tired, having driven the kids back to the cabin in Woodstock, disgusted with Paula's continuing foolishness (What did you give them to eat, Jesse? The usual, I answer, chocolate bars, popcorn and steaks), quiet in the car, empty of kids and toys and food, Lisa says, "Oh, Jesse."

February 22.
My prostate infection has returned after a ten-year absence. The burning in the peeing, the tickling, the visit to the doctor, the indignity of him sticking his finger up my ass and palpating a gland inside that makes me scream out in pain. Tender, he says. Three pills a day, a daily bath (I haven't taken a bath in ages), no alcohol and cut down on fucking, from nightly to at least every-other-nightly, he says, and it'll get better in proportion to the lack of irritation fucking brings to this condition. Less fucking and it gets better faster, he says. Is he evil? Is he to be believed? How can a Dr. Goodstein know how mystically, physically, philosophically, joyously I've been into fucking lately. The devil brought my prostate infection. There is no God, otherwise he wouldn't subject me to prostate infections if he gave

a shit about his creations. Maybe he's a malevolent God. Or just one of many. No, none. There is none. Don't get sidetracked.

Lisa says I talk about Paula too much.

Lisa feels like she can't get through my Paula pre-occupation, but I tell her fourteen days is a record. And she knows when I'm not seeing her I'm not fucking anyone else, probably because of my prick condition. She says she may have cystitis now. She told me she once had fourteen different kinds of vaginal infections, nonvenereal, at the same time and then developed an allergy to some cream she was taking in addition to twenty-eight pills a day, making ulcerated sores that would break and run down her legs and the whole mess so bad that she couldn't walk for three days and she was starving alone till some friends brought food and drink, and two of her roommates had crabs at the time and left their towels around the bathroom and she thought, Oh God, if I get crabs in my ulcerated open cunt sores I'll kill myself. Her roommates fled as though she was a leper.

Lisa doesn't know what to make out of it when I tell her she's such a good poet. She hasn't let me read much, but what I have read is very, very good poetry—the images, the sensitivity, the whole soft, romantic texture in them. She can't accept it may be true that she's a very good poet, just like her self-denial stuff when I tell her she has terrific breasts, that I find them beautiful to gaze upon. She said of her breasts once, "I find them inoffensive." *Inoffensive?*

She said she'd make curtains for me when she buys her sewing machine next week. She doesn't like to buy clothes (identity crises and such) and prefers to make them, wear castoffs from her sister. She has said she'd like to be a minister, or be in the Peace Corps, but knows both are out. I tell her to be a good poet and she doesn't know I mean it.

The kids and Lisa and I went to see *Fantasia* and we all loved it. Had apples and cheese in a restaurant down the street from the theater after. In the bus on the way home Tom gets into a conversation with a little old Jewish lady, telling her about dinosaurs and flying horses and the movie. "My father's good at making up stories like that," he tells her. "That's what he is—a storyteller." Proudly, he said it, I think.

All you people out there who have a lot of people in your life, in your home, in your work, with you. I sit here alone. No one else is here. Except a dog, and

she is what she is, not another person. One day we
will learn something more about aloneness and loneliness. It's probably a cause, or effect, of all kinds of
mental illness. It's also where the thing called inspiration happens, in writing, painting, composing,
inventing. Alone. No one else. It often makes you
doubt yourself, and your sanity, that it's all going on
out there with other people and you aren't with
them, you just aren't with them and seeing it when
you're alone.

Fruitlessly, I keep asking myself if my prick problem is divine punishment. Or self-punishment. I now
take two baths a day, sitting there and sitting there
and sitting there. I ought to put the television set in
the bathroom.

Says Lisa: "I have friends who have had chronic
cystitis for years and years. Now *that's* really awful.
That's much worse than what you have."

Hearing about people who suffer more than me
never has the effect of cheering me up much.

Of *Waiting*, Lisa says it's a trip, that it started off
in reality and then took off into the phantasmagori-
cal.

A day in the life. I would like to be able to think
I have captured a period of life, a period of time,

and got it right. Except I feel I never do. I feel I could write all my life and not get on paper what living sixty seconds—any stop-time sixty seconds—is like. The whole crowding of sensations. What you hear, see, think, sense, and where you are. Any seconds of it. Write it so it takes sixty seconds to read. The danger being you could write those seconds and it would take the length of a book to read.

It scares Lisa to see that Paula and I could have lived together eight or nine years and now treat each other so badly, as though neither of us really exist.

"Jesse," she says, "you ought to get a good bed that won't hurt your back, and move to the country, breathe fresh air, and stop smoking."

"And quit fucking."

"Only temporarily."

Lisa smokes like a fiend. Marlboros.

Three weeks ago, with Terry, I had an erection that wouldn't go away; it lingered on for an hour after we finished making love. I couldn't do anything with it and finally went into the bathroom and still stoned thought, Shit, what am I going to do about this? I decided to put cold water on it. Stupido! Maybe I gave it a chill. Pneumonia. I ought to ask the doctor.

A dream of angrily attacking my father at the
dinner table. He is eating. A girl is there. "Look,"
I scream at him, "I don't need you. I am insulting
you. I don't care if you're here or not. Give me back
my safety deposit key. . . . You're not welcome
here. . . ." Things like that. He sits there eating,
ignoring my outburst. But I don't say, "Get out, don't
ever call me, don't ever come back."

It was brought on by his phone call yesterday.
The fourth from them since the long letter I sent.
The first two came from my mother. She said she
was sick, sounding weak and failing, told me about
her brother-in-law dying in the hospital from a can-
cerous prostate, of his loving children (and my father) standing deathwatch over his bed (the two
children, incidentally, son, thirty-six, and daughter,
thirty, living at home with parents in Brooklyn). "If
I had to read your letter a second time, I'd die of a
broken heart," she said. "That's what you want, isn't
it? For us to die." She cried. In her second phone call
she asked to see my shrink, as though I were a six-
year-old with the mumps and she wanted to consult
the doctor with me to find out what was wrong with
her little boy.

In my father's phone call he said he read and reread my letter many times and pleaded guilty to a lot
in it, said it made him see some things for the first

time, made him regret a lot, and then he offered to
pay my shrink bills, wanted to see me and talk to
me. But I didn't want to see him, to rehash it all, to
be his therapist, to hear apologies and regrets. Nothing.

But on his second call:

"How are you feeling?" he asked.

"I don't want to discuss the state of my health."

"What's the good word? And good news?"

"Good news and bad."

"What's the bad news? What's the good news?"

"I don't want to discuss any of it with you."

"Jesse, there are some toys here from one time
the children were up here. And two typewriters of
yours."

"I'm not coming up to retrieve them."

"What shall I do with them?"

"Give them away or throw them away."

"Not a big, expensive electric typewriter I won't."

"That's up to you."

"I'll bring it down to your place."

"It's too heavy for you to carry."

"I won't *shlep* it. I'll take a cab."

"I don't want to put you through the expense."

"So you can reimburse me then."

"Would you like that?"

"I wouldn't take your money. I'm only kidding."

"Fine."

"Have you had any mail from Ben lately?"

"No."

"We neither."

"Mm."

"How are you feeling?"

"You asked me that already. How are you and mother feeling?"

"Trying to stay healthy, to keep our health, taking it easy, not doing anything much, anything at all."

"Mm."

"Are you still seeing your, eh, that . . . uh . . . three times a week?"

"Yes."

"So, eh, how are you feeling?"

"Look. What do you care about the state of my health? Why do you keep asking? What are you trying to ask me?"

"I'm interested in how you are. I care about how you are."

"I don't care if you care or not."

"That doesn't stop me from caring."

"Okay."

"What's Tommy's address in Woodstock? I'd like to send him a post card."

"He's in New York."

"Oh? I'd like to see him. I'd like to talk to him. How could we arrange that?"

"He could call you sometime when he's here."

"Would you do that please?"

"I'll try to remember."

"I'd appreciate it. Well Jesse, it's been nice talking to you."

"What are you talking about? It hasn't been nice talking to me. I've been insulting, abrupt, rude and discourteous, and you say it's been *nice* talking to me?"

"No, no, I mean it when I say it's been nice talking to you, hearing your voice and so forth, speaking with you."

Horrible.

IX

from notebook five

I have been getting angry at Janet. (She and that guy used to say I never showed my anger, even in their offices.) She was saying I haven't been so patient and tolerant and indulgent with Paula. I screamed that I have so. She said also that I shouldn't subject girlfriends to having to see our relationship close up, to see my contempt and coldness and anger so close up. I agree with her. Lisa thought it was unwise for her, too, but only after the fact. And then Janet suggested that my priapism and prostatitis were emotional problems. I was angry at her for suggesting something like that when she didn't know it for a fact, that all raising a question like that does is unsettle me more. What was the point of it? How do you know? I shouted. She ad-

mitted she didn't but was only suggesting, not saying
it for a fact.

"Rosie, it'll be just like it was with us at the start
—you at the till and me at the engine," Humphrey
Bogart to Katherine Hepburn as they sally forth to
torpedo the *Luisa* in *The African Queen*.

The mayor of Utica was on television last night
on the Dick Cavett Show. Imagine, having the
mayor of Utica in my living room. See his face. Hear
him. Get to know him. Television is amazing.
Haven't watched it in months.

Paula and I talked about our divorcing stalemate
in a Bronx apartment, in the company of two seconds, observers, peacemakers. Arnie. And Larry, her
macrobiotic-freak-Yoga teacher. She agreed to $5,-
200 a year, increased only by the cost of living index
increase, this dough hers to get at the beginning of
the year. She did a good bit of storming out of the
room and they kept calling her back in. It relieves
me of writing checks weekly, relieves me of thinking
in terms of sliding scale incomes. She can move and
live anywhere she wants but I get together with the
kids for a period totaling a quarter of the year if we

live far apart geographically, like for example, New
York and California. (If she moved that way, it
would be awful. I don't know what would happen.
I tried to get her to say—as did the others there—
whether she had any plans for moving away. She
was evasive.) I don't know what would be our relationship—mine and the kids—if we lived that far
apart. I just don't know how it would work out, except that I can't demand she live within a hundred
miles of me for the next fifteen years. All my problems about the kids, however, would be solved if I
had them living with me, by virtue of my winning a
custody suit, or if she were dead. I think she'd have
to do something more progressively crazy and bla-
tant before I—recent suicide attempt and all—could
win a custody suit. As far as her being dead is concerned, I really couldn't arrange that in reality, only
in fantasy.

Lisa and my underwear.
We were lying in bed, talking, after making love
on my Castro convertible. Kidding around. She said
she wore nightgowns. I said I wore underwear. Yes,
she said, but you can't make love with your underwear on. But I have, I said, hundreds of times, especially in the winter.
She jumped out of bed. For the next half hour
she insulted me, abused me, attacked me, threw everything in the book at me. Called me names.

It was weird.

Finally, we went back over it all to see what this was all about. I had been talking about my undershirt. She thought I meant underpants. She thought I meant sticking my prick through the windows and fucking that way. She built up this whole image of years of inhuman fucking, that I was some kind of pervert-monster.

When we cleared up the misunderstanding, I yelled at her, "How could you even think I could do a thing like that?"

She didn't say. She must suspect me of things.

Lisa's insecurity, and her various accusations about my shortcomings are getting difficult to take. She either better stop, or we will stop. What are the nature of these accusations?

Karen, on the phone: giving Paula $5,200 a year will make her hate me, be bitter toward me always, and as a result the children will hate me. I don't think it will work that way for Paula; for Karen maybe. Paula doesn't seem to mind the changes in her "material" circumstances.

It's too bad to have your life fucked up by something you have no control over, as in Tom and Suzie's case; as in Jesse's and his parents.

I've invited this seventeen-year-old baby-sitter to go away with me and the kids for the weekend. I want to seduce her, and I think she's been angling at seducing me as well. Suppose I do. Then what? Time passes and I go after this fifteen-year-old, right? Interesting. More times passes and I get a hankering for this beautiful thirteen-year-old. And then a twelve-year-old. Where does it end? Is it perverse? What is this thing about? Is it because of the remembered frustration of not finding girls to make love with during my adolescence? I ought to see a psychiatrist.

What will they look like,
The lungs of the people
Who died
And smoked grass all their lives?
Like the lungs of cancer victims
And cigarette tobacco types?
Or different?
It will be a long time
Before we have an authoritative report.

Lisa: I feel dirty when my hair is dirty.

Last week Tommy and I had a major metaphysical discussion. It came up as a result of his asking about the Beatles record jacket title, "Rubber Soul." What do they mean, "rubber soul"? What do they mean by "soul"?

"It's inside you, you can't see it, it's what makes you feel good, it's what makes you feel bad, it's the whole part of you that you know is there but that you can't see, it's the force that makes you do things, it's the part of you that you can't touch or put your finger on."

A discussion to that effect. All of which he understood. What a colossal cool person he is going to be. At five he is informed and can speak sensibly and sensitively on the soul, the Panther breakfast program, cops, the army, Vietnam, Christ, Krishna, sperms meeting eggs, and acid freaks.

I read him my three children books. I finally wrote them.

They are: *The Boy and the Alligator, The Green Creature* and *The Boy Who Carried the Wounded Bird*. One is an adventure story, the other about a child's senses (I think), and the latter a peace fable.

Yet to come are *How the Dog and the Squirrel Became Friends, How the Knight and the Dragon*

Became Friends. I'm not sure I'm really interested in doing them, but I might.

My life is entirely different as a result of my answering service. It's a whole other dimension.

March 20.

Janet frequently eats lunch during our sessions. What about the things she doesn't write down when she is eating. What if she wasn't eating and wrote them down? I'm not sure how I feel about her eating lunch during our sessions.

To say she didn't care for the parents coming up to see the kids at my place is an understatement. They just called up when the kids were there and Tommy answered the phone and they pleaded with me to come up and see them. There was nothing prearranged about it. They came up, and I went over to Lisa's house and I took a nap and then went back to my place and then they left. Seeing their grandchildren every other month or so, like that, would be tolerable to me—but apparently not to Janet, if I understand Janet. Is it at this point in my "cure" that Janet thinks it's bad for me to see them? Or forever? Is it so terrible that they probably saw two toothbrushes in the bathroom? They asked me questions and I supplied no information. I assume they grilled Tommy as to his life and circumstances and he may have said whatever he said. But I don't care what they heard, or what they think about it. And should they give voice to it I don't have to listen. Janet seems to find something wrong in all this, and I'm not sure I understand. In fact, I don't understand.

My relationship with my answering service is embarrassingly formal. Should I try to fix it up? They do this whole "Mr. Jacobi" and "Sir" business like the machine-operators at the phone company. Should I tell them to call me "Jesse" and that it's just an exchange of services—I pay some money and they give me messages and the money I pay pays them? I assume they know all kinds of things about my personal life by now so isn't it idiotic to go through this "Mister" and "Sir" routine?

We had a beautiful and spontaneous party on the first day of spring. Started inviting people at one in the afternoon. Thirty came.

I want to write and direct a movie about revolutionary alligators in the New York City sewers and a bunch of radicals who find them one day while hiding out from the law. How the two groups conspire to take over the city.

Is Lisa making dinner tonight?

I will go to Yoga class at four fifteen, walk the dog at six. Eat dinner which Lisa is cooking. After which we will go to the movies.

Lisa's friend brought her shrink pictures of her childhood, her family, her little girl snapshots. She dwelt on her mother's pictures, amazed at how she progressively, in five years, seemed to freeze up into an overly made-up, haughty, icy, society-looking, phony-smile person. Lisa's friend seemed very upset.

I had a dream about Paula not having a date and calling me up and I didn't have a date either. She suggests we spend the evening together, to which I shout, *No*, are you crazy? that's the last thing I want to do. I believe I really feel that way consciously, too.

One change: recently some sleeplessness. Recently so many things have happened that I occasionally have trouble sleeping; excitement about future, and future possibilities, like the house upstate, a trip to Mexico for the divorce, to California for a screen-

play job, a summer trip to Europe, a new car, making
a movie.

Some of what I do—like the overseas trip, the
new car, the house and land—depends on whether
all this money actually happens. There is an offer
for a movie screenplay which I haven't decided
about yet, but which would mean over $25,000 or so,
and the paperback sale on the book could be $40,-
000 or $100,000, or much less, or nothing.

So, feeling good, I called Bud up on the phone. In
London. After midnight it was only $4.00 for the
first three minutes, $1.35 each additional minute.
Seems cheap.

How is Ireland and Scotland in the summer? I
ask.

How is your marriage?

He is having an exhibit in Montreal in September, his wife is old-fashioned solid, he likes his work
and what's happening with it, his wife is going to
Tunis, he needs to be alone more: report from
Buddy.

There are new orange drapes in the apartment—
fabric from the 14th Street store and put together
by the folks at Neet Cleaners, hardware installation
by the author. And Indian madras throw covers all

over the apartment. The place looks much better. Lisa's had something to do with it.

Lisa cares for school and she doesn't care for school. She says she wasn't going to go back this year, last September. She likes getting "A's" and she likes to learn. She dislikes being called a chick. She likes afternoon naps. She avoids leaving her name with my answering service. Lisa. When she answers the phone, she says "Hi" very softly, a tinkle-twinkle, ladylike softness.

She has a beautiful body.

She has a beautiful body.

Her skin is so soft, so baby-soft, I can touch her and kiss her for long, long, long times.

"Hey, Mister Tambourine Man," she grew up on Dylan, for God's sake. I didn't. What's it like growing up on Dylan?

She's twenty-two. She's a child.

Her twenty-two is ten years older than Paula's thirty-one years.

Her twenty-two is also younger than Paula's fifteen years.

Out Paula.

One very beautiful person is helping me get finished with you. Finally finished.

She is doing other things, too; more; but she's also doing that.

I wonder what this beautiful person writes about me.

Does she write that she loves me? Or does she, like me, deny to write it?

I cried.

First time in a long time.

Last time in the hospital.

That's a long time.

Molly hasn't been walked.

I bought Lisa a colorful thing today.

April 6.

Bought an oriental carpet today.

Who or what do I have to thank for the fact that Lisa Bergson came into my life, Lisa who has made me, is making me, so very happy. Even though we both have sore throats and budding coughs. Most of all of everything we do I like making love with her the most—more than her mind, more than shooting movies, which I do a lot now (trusty old 8mm Sankyo), which I enjoy as much as writing, possibly. She is lovely. She is like a little girl one moment and the next moment the world's most sophisticated lover, a pouting, unhappy child one hour and a little later wrapping her knees around my ears as we finish making love and looking at me that way of hers.

April 10.

Did that really happen? It was supernatural.

I was over at Steve's, buying an ounce of his newest and finest reefer. I had an allergic reaction to
his *kif* the day before, itchy eyes and tearing, like hay
fever when I was a kid. So I told him I couldn't use
the *kif*. We made a deal: twenty-five dollars instead
of thirty-five dollars for my new stuff. Okay with me.
But don't say anything, he said. Some people are
coming over who're paying thirty-five dollars for it.
First a black guy comes, George. Cool. Nice. Lisa
was wearing this sexy dress that left her bare white
arms naked filling the room somehow.

Bell rings.

Steve to his partner: "You know this guy?"

No, the last time he sent a kid to pick it up. I
never seen him before. He's Al's friend.

A big guy comes in.

No.

It can't be.

It is!

Doctor Nathanson. Doctor Jack Nathanson. Ex-
shrink.

I see him three or four seconds before he sees me
sitting there. I am on a couch, quietly zonked.

"Good God," I hear myself say.

He stands there looking at me.

I say, "The world is populated by only one hundred and seventy-four people, I'm sure of it."

"No, there are eight million people in New York,"
he says.

He is red-faced and stunned.

"No, one hundred and seventy-four," I repeat. "That's the entire population."

He looks at Steve. "I, uh, I'm late. I can't stay. I have an opening to catch, a premiere. Someone gave me tickets." He takes out money.

"What picture?" I ask.

Getting Straight, he says. He shows me his passes.

"Elliott Gould in that?"

"Yes."

A pause.

"Oh, Jack, this is Lisa. Jack is your first name, right?"

Nothing more is said. He is incredibly jittery. He pays. He jumps up, smiles nervously at us. He turns to leave and in the middle of the living room smashes his head on a hanging metal light fixture. Crash. He grabs his forehead. Everyone gasps.

"Are you all right?" asks Steve's girlfriend.

He must feel as bad and small and dumb as the last time he wet his bed. He smiles nervously at the crowd of onlookers and keeps heading for the door.

Door closes.

"What an incredibly uptight man," says Lisa.

Steve looks at me.

"Who is dat guy, Jesse? What was 'at about? You know him?"

My ex-shrink, I tell the assembled. I saw him four

months last year. I still owe him a $180 bill, and I
don't think I'm going to pay him because he was
such a bad shrink. He didn't render any services.

"What was that opening business?" asks Lisa.

"His girl reviews movies," I say.

"Yeah, dat's right," says Steve. "She reviews
movies."

We sit, six of us, stunned by the coincidence. Every thirty seconds or so, Steve shakes his head. "Dat
was fantastic. I don't believe it. . . . It's spooky.
Your shink. . . . Holy shit."

His grass cost him five dollars more than a fifty-
minute session with me.

Robert Green. Publisher of my anthology, publisher of cookbooks and children's books. Called him
up.

We can go up to his place in the Adirondacks and
take a look around for real estate from there. He is
two and a half hours north of Albany. He suggests
the Middlebury, Vermont, area. He told me all
about his frost line and why his pipes freeze and I
didn't understand any of it. If I don't mind hauling
water, he says, I can go up there. I won't mind hauling water, Bob.

Lisa, let's go to Bob's place, haul water, get
stoned, and look for real estate, a summer farm. Bob
often tells me about his re-entry problems in the sum-

mer; after he spends a month up there, he's thinking about how to set up his publishing office in the
Adirondacks and never come back to the city (even
though he *lives* on Long Island), and that's when I
know it's time to come back, he says. Once you stay
up that way a while, he tells me, you'll say fuckit to
the city. Who knows?

I'd like to paint in the country. I would really
and truly like to do some water colors outdoors, or
Dri-marker stuff. I've already started doing some in-
door painting and drawing—first time in fifteen years
or so.

April 15.
Yesterday I showed the shrink two hours' worth of
home movies from 1966 to the present, with Paula
fat and jolly, Tommy playing with the puppies, two
Fire Island summers, Suzie as an infant, the Virgin
Islands trip. About two thousand feet of film. A
double session.

Janet:

"Paula looked sad in the last reel."

"Almost the only time you see Paula in the films
is when she's there with Tommy."

"The movies are about Tommy."

"There's no doubt who your first love was—
Tommy."

"You took lots of pictures of Lisa that you never took of Paula."

At the Bryant Park rally, I shot a lot of good film. Youth Against War and Fascism tried to attack the speaker's platform and take it away from William Kunstler and Pete Seeger. The Gay Liberation Front also charged the speaker's platform.

I'm smoking the eye-itching *kif* again. Don't know why. I'm starting to feel guilty about the amount of grass I'm smoking. There must be some reason for that.

I like the way Lisa says *toke*. She does a lot with the word, like she does with *dart* and *tart*.

I help you glow, Lisa says.
Aren't you glowing more since you know me?
You're a positive experience.

A massacre at Kent State.
Unbelievable.

The revolution is occurring.
The Dow Jones dropped 19 points.
Are we entering a historic few days?

New Haven, Connecticut.
What would the people who founded this country think of the fact that in two hundred years we would be interfering in a war in Indochina and murdering people and telling people there how they can and can't live.

Jerry Rubin in a cape telling students to stop going to school, that it was pointless. (Two days ago a newscaster called it, on NBC, "the Southeast Asian War." Not the Vietnam war any more.)

In the evening at the apartment of a friend of Lisa's we hear thud-thud-thud from a distance. We get in the car and drive down for a look. Came around the corner, approaching Yale, for a look; a street barricaded by a long line of soldiers with their guns across their chests. I slowed down and stopped in the turn. "Excuse me, Lieutenant, I seen to have made a wrong turn. Could you tell me what country this is?" Tear gas firing all around the Gothic buildings. An arrest or two. Jeeps and armed soldiers everywhere. Whose country is this? But no mowing down of children like in Ohio.

The Panther rally was held on a big lawn on a beautiful spring day. With fifteen thousand people waving their fists, standing and cheering, the smell of grass drifting over from everywhere, it made you feel we could really win.

On Sunday we drove to Vermont. Rupert. I rented a thirty-six-acre farm of pine groves, hill pastures, brook, woodlands of birch and spruce. A hilltop with a twenty-mile view of farms and mountains. Rented it for mid-May till the end of June.

How does the wind come? asked Tommy when he was five.

Where does the wind come from? he asked when he was three.

We're a little more cosmic than before.

Tommy: Suzie's diaper came dancing into the room and left two craps on Jack's shoulders.

Suzie turned into her diaper.

Tommy likes the idea about Suzie and her diapers. He says I should write a children's book about it, with Suzie saying, "I'm full of pee-pee and crap."

We could together write a pornographic children's book. Mr. Belly-button Tommy wrote it. He likes the idea.

I just thought about my prick problem. It's gone.
Disappeared.

May 13.

I was divorced in sleepy Juarez a few days ago.
Across the Rio Grande River from sleepy El Paso,
America. My lawyer there says he has handled a
quarter million divorces and a taxi driver offered to
take me to a really good show, flashing me yellow and
brown teeth. Went to Los Angeles with Lisa after.

Did I forget to say "I undo"?

She met a movie mogul or two with me. She was
impressed with how stupid they are.

I am divorced.

A beautiful drive up the coast to San Francisco.
On the cable car I pretended I was a psychiatrist
and had a discussion with a little fat lady whose
chest button said she was from Topeka, Kansas,
and attending the American Psychiatric Association
convention. I asked her if she were here for the convention and she said yes, looking me over; Are you?
I told her I was, and she said, New York? and yes.
Do you have a private practice or are you in a hospital? Private, I said. My husband's with the Men-
ninger, she said. For the next ten minutes we dis-

Never

cussed the teen-age dope problem in Kansas and New York. I made up all kinds of statistics and facts. Lisa was angry at me for doing it.

Every other hitchhiker picked up in California offered us dope, friendly, to sample, to buy. Very authentic long-haired blond freaks out there.

We stayed at the Beverly Wilshire in Los Angeles, courtesy of Twentieth Century-Fox, on a bed that was a city-block big. At Berkeley, on a Sunday afternoon, we watched amazed during an outdoor jam session as two campus cops picked a kid out of the two hundred or so sitting around and hauled him off. Nobody did anything about it. They must be too used to it out here. In New York, at NYU or Columbia, the campus cops couldn't get away with that.

California! The place is terrific, but too full of loonies and cops. Yay. Some dude. That gives me a weird flash. When they see me all they see is clouds and darkness, man. Cop a lid. A friend of mine at Berkeley had her knee blown off by a tear-gas canister. The pig-cops are raping hippie girls out here. Far out. Everything is far out in California. That's the way they talk. Yay.

The grass I smoked in California was better than most of the grass I smoked in New York this past year. And cheaper. Half price.

The night after Lisa flew back I camped out under a canopy of sequoia. Under it, above me, an opening looks like a map of South America, a whitish-gray, light blue sky peeking through black foliage a hundred feet up. San Mateo State Park. Camping grounds deserted. Out of two hundred sites, only three or four seem taken.

This is a strange thing for me to be doing.

Twenty or thirty feet below there's a noisy stream. Like a running water faucet.

I tried to go down, at night, but the drop, and I couldn't see. The hill was so steep I nearly tumbled down. I held trees, roots, ferns, anything anchored and rooted. Squatting and sliding.

I went back up, lay down, and smoked a joint. Just came in off the boat last week, the hitchhiker said. Andy.

The sky above me is not open. The branches and their leaves hide most of it. The leaves are so dense. Through openings seeing clowns and Americas and rabbits.

Praise be to you, Lisa Bergson.

Those trees must be more than a hundred feet. Like Jack's beanstalks. They're pretty much straight-up trees and they end somewhere in the sky. Which is the tallest tree? There are signs. I'll look in the morning.

The moon is low, from where I am lying.

But God only knows what direction I am facing.

It is not cold. Fresh air drifts and floats all over my face.

No animals making noise here. The only sound is the running stream. And the last sputters of my fire. I broke up a lot of wood for it.

I did Yoga eye exercises at the trees and sky. And then I fell asleep.

I awoke.

It seems darker.

It's like being in the bottom of a high-domed church, inside, and looking up at the cupola, only here the ceiling is the leaves. Are the leaves.

No hyenas or night-calling animals.

Why?

This is like going to another place. Anybody who has ever slept in a sequoia forest will know what I mean.

Have you ever slept under a sequoia tree stoned?

Morning. The tall trees are practically shaking, vibrating, from all these shrieking, whistling, clicking, crying wake-up calling birds.

I'm getting too much happiness, too many things are going well, too much good will—and I'm going to get crucified for it. I seem to be in some state of permanent high. I seem to be some kind of influence on people these days.

Tomorrow Lisa and I go up to the farm in Vermont.

Alligators: the film. Can we use the sewers? The costume should be life-sized. Green Mountain Boys—archers, guerrilla training in the mountains. How much the animal handler and his alligators? For two days. Whose flooded basement? Revolutionary war costumes. Do blanks make a muzzle flash?

Why don't I remember my dreams hardly ever any more? Why are so many things suddenly possible for me? Journey inside and outside. Answer: some compound of the shrink, Lisa, dope, Yoga, time, me.

A friend of Lisa's, living in Sweden, sent her a translation of an article from a Swedish newspaper's book section saying I was a better writer than this one and that. Very flattering. My first was didactic,

they said, the second Kafkaesque, the third my best.
The Swedes.

Buy cork.

June 16. I love my new Scout. International
Harvester. It goes up mountainsides and across
meadows.

Up here on the second floor, sitting by the window on the floor. An overgrown lawn, fifty yards of
grass and then a barbed-wire fence. A boy with a
kite standing there, reeling in line. In front of him
a cornfield, the stalks from last year withered and
brown. At the end of the cornfield a row of trees,
and beyond the trees a grassy field spotted with
dandelions. And then hills of trees and mountains of
trees beyond. A lot of sky. A nervous-looking black
shepherd floats into the picture, loping and sniffing.
The latter Molly, the former Tom.

Clink-clink sounds downstairs. Suzie talking with
Lisa in the kitchen, and Judy Collins singing "Hey,
That's No Way to Say Good-Bye."

Noises out the window, birds tuning up, a stream,

and Tommy, imitating Lennon as he reels in string. Winds swishing the trees. "Am hungry," says the kid downstairs. Lennon lines from the kid in the field.

In a minute he runs toward the house with the reeled-in string and the kite. The horse is tethered under a young maple and he stops to talk. I can't hear the conversation. He turns to the house and runs a zigzag path across the field. Suzie comes out the door and they confront each other blowing kisses so violently that Suzie falls down.

Hey, I call down. You know what you were doing all the time you were reeling in the kite?

What? He is mystified.

Singing Beatles songs to yourself.

Ohhhhh. . . . I was not.

I bought the farm in Halsey.

Suspicions about insanity. No more. Better.

Two dogs sleeping together over there by the fireplace. Sheba and Molly, mother and daughter, happily reunited.

"Good morning, London, this is the United States calling. Do you have a listing for a Bud Seymour?"

Talking to him at two o'clock in the morning from a Vermont farmhouse. The overseas operator is in White Plains, she tells me.

I am a nice person, and if only people would be nice to me . . .

Adventures in the Here and the Hereafter, by—

I moved into my new place in Halsey July 1. The summer is so green and sweet there are days that seem like the Moslem's idea of paradise. A stream bubbles down out of a steep hillside of birch and evergreen, right by the side of the barn. The bees buzzing. The grassy sloping meadow behind the house, strewn with boulders and pine. Every week different wildflowers appear—yellow and then violet and then orange flowers and red ones. Cows from the next pasture nibble grass while I sit at the fence beneath them and read them my morning's work. I bought a white horse and ride her several times a week, all day sometimes, up into the hills and over pine carpets and over old logging trails through forests. Many nights I make pictures all over the sky, connecting the dots among the stars. The last thing I hear at night is the water bubbling around the rocks under my window. Every morning at six the birds wake me. All that is missing is the shepherd's flute.

Ovaltine, honey, cheese, crunchy Granola: eat it a lot.

I spend more time horseback riding than I do writing and fucking combined.